Framework

9

MATHS

A

Ray Allan

Martin Williams

Claire Perry

OXFORD

UNIVERSITY PRESS

OXFORD
UNIVERSITY PRESS

Great Clarendon Street, Oxford OX2 6DP

Oxford University Press is a department of the University of Oxford.
It furthers the University's objective of excellence in research,
scholarship, and education by publishing worldwide in

Oxford New York

Auckland Cape Town Dar es Salaam Hong Kong Karachi
Kuala Lumpur Madrid Melbourne Mexico City Nairobi
New Delhi Shanghai Taipei Toronto

With offices in

Argentina Austria Brazil Chile Czech Republic France Greece
Guatemala Hungary Italy Japan Poland Portugal Singapore
South Korea Switzerland Thailand Turkey Ukraine Vietnam

Oxford is a registered trade mark of Oxford University Press
in the UK and in certain other countries

British Library Cataloguing in Publication Data

Data available

ISBN-10: 019 914 973 9
ISBN-13: 978 019 914 973 5

10 9 8 7 6 5 4 3 2 1

Typeset by Mathematical Composition Setters Ltd.

Printed in Italy by Rotolito Lombarda

Acknowledgements

The photograph on the cover is reproduced courtesy of Pictor.

The Publisher would like to thank the following for permission to reproduce
photographs:

P1 Michael Taylor/OUP; p14 Alessandro Trovati/AP/Empics;
p20 Michael Taylor/OUP; p24 Simon Ritter/Alamy Images;
p25 Chris Young/PA/Empics; p51 Alan Copson City Pictures/Alamy Images;
p85 Peter Jordan/PA/Empics; p103 Martin Rickett/PA/Empics;
p113 Brand X Pictures/OUP; p122 Robert Harding Pictures;
p147l Dennis Frates/Alamy Images; p147r Corbis/Digital Stock/OUP;
p154 Volkswagen AG; p156 Gareth Fuller/PA/Empics;
p158 Michael Taylor/OUP; p203 Michael Taylor/OUP;
p206 Michael Taylor/OUP; p214 Michael Taylor/OUP.

Figurative artwork is by Paul Daviz

About this book

This book has been specifically written for students who will be working at Level 4 in Year 9. It is designed to help students consolidate their achievement at Levels 3 and 4 and progress to Level 5. The content leads to the 3–5 tier of entry in the NC tests. The content is also designed to provide access to the Support Book in the same series and the two books can be used along side each other in the classroom.

The authors are experienced teachers who have been working with students of a similar ability for years and so are well qualified to provide appropriate classroom practice.

The book is made up of units that provide access to the Support tier of the sample medium term plans that complement the Framework for Teaching Mathematics at KS3.

The units are:

The last four units in this book are designed to consolidate KS3 work and bridge to KS4 work.

Each unit comprises double page spreads that should take a lesson to teach. These are shown on the full contents list.

Problem solving is integrated throughout the material as suggested in the Framework.

This book is made up of units of work which are colour coded into: Algebra (Blue), Data (Pink), Number (Orange), Shape, space and measures (Green), Problem solving (Light Green) and a Bridging unit (Red).

Each unit of work starts with an overview of the content of the unit, as specified in the Primary Framework document, so that you know exactly what you are expected to learn.

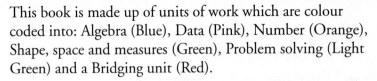

This unit will show you how to:

▶▶ Recognise and extend number sequences.

▶▶ Generate and describe simple integer sequences using term-to-term and position-to-term rules.

▶▶ Generate and describe sequences from practical contexts.

▶▶ Recognise and explain patterns and relationships.

The first page of a unit also highlights the skills and facts you should already know and provides Check in questions to help you revise before you start so that you are ready to apply the knowledge later in the unit:

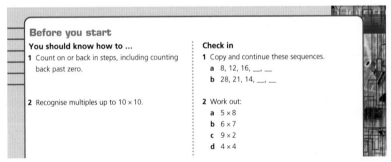

Before you start

You should know how to ...

1 Count on or back in steps, including counting back past zero.

2 Recognise multiples up to 10 × 10.

Check in

1 Copy and continue these sequences.
 a 8, 12, 16, __, __
 b 28, 21, 14, __, __

2 Work out:
 a 5 × 8
 b 6 × 7
 c 9 × 2
 d 4 × 4

Inside each unit, the content develops in double page spreads which all follow the same structure.

The spreads start with a list of the learning outcomes and a summary of the keywords:

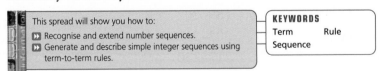

This spread will show you how to:

▶▶ Recognise and extend number sequences.

▶▶ Generate and describe simple integer sequences using term-to-term rules.

KEYWORDS

Term   Rule

Sequence

The keywords are summarised and defined in a Glossary at the end of the book so you can always check what they mean.

Key information is highlighted in the text so you can see the facts you need to learn.

▶ To describe a sequence you need a start number and the rule.

Examples showing the key skills and techniques you need to develop are shown in boxes. Also hint boxes show tips and reminders you may find useful:

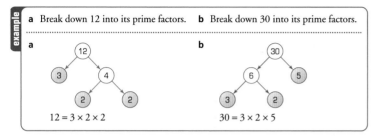

a Break down 12 into its prime factors.   **b** Break down 30 into its prime factors.

$12 = 3 \times 2 \times 2$

$30 = 3 \times 2 \times 5$

Each exercise is carefully graded, set at three levels of difficulty:

1. The first few questions provide lead-in questions, revising previous learning.
2. The questions in the middle of the exercise provide the main focus of the material.
3. The last few questions are challenging questions that provide a link to the Support tier learning objectives.

At the end of each unit is a summary page so that you can revise the learning of the unit before moving on.

Check out questions are provided to help you check your understanding of the key concepts covered and your ability to apply the key techniques. They are all based on actual Key Stage 3 past paper questions so they give you practice at the standard required in your examination.

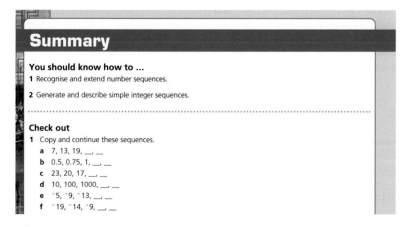

Summary

You should know how to ...
1 Recognise and extend number sequences.

2 Generate and describe simple integer sequences.

Check out
1 Copy and continue these sequences.
   a 7, 13, 19, __, __
   b 0.5, 0.75, 1, __, __
   c 23, 20, 17, __, __
   d 10, 100, 1000, __, __
   e ⁻5, ⁻9, ⁻13, __, __
   f ⁻19, ⁻14, ⁻9, __, __

The answers to the Check in and Check out questions are produced at the end of the book so that you can check your own progress and identify any areas that need work.

Contents

This unit will show you how to:

▶▶ Recognise and extend number sequences.

▶▶ Generate and describe simple integer sequences using term-to-term and position-to-term rules.

▶▶ Generate and describe sequences from practical contexts.

▶▶ Recognise and explain patterns and relationships.

Times make a sequence: 1 o'clock, 2 o'clock, 3 o'clock …

Before you start

You should know how to …

1 Count on or back in steps, including counting back past zero.

2 Recognise multiples up to 10 × 10.

3 Find differences.

Check in

1 Copy and continue these sequences.

   a 8, 12, 16, __, __

   b 28, 21, 14, __, __

2 Work out:

   a 5 × 8

   b 6 × 7

   c 9 × 2

   d 4 × 4

3 Find the difference between these numbers.

   a 8 and 5

   b 18 and 14

   c 13 and 9

   d 17 and 8

This spread will show you how to:

▶▶ Recognise and extend number sequences.
▶▶ Generate and describe simple integer sequences using term-to-term rules.

KEYWORDS
Term   Rule
Sequence

The door numbers in this street go up by 2 each time.

The next door number will be 11 + 2 = 13.

The door numbers make a sequence: 7, 9, 11, 13, ...

The rule for the sequence is:

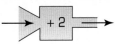

You can count the door numbers backwards.
This reverses the sequence: 13, 11, 9, 7, ...

The rule is:

▶ **To describe a sequence you need a start number and the rule.**

These patterns of tiles make a sequence:

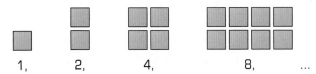

1,   2,   4,   8,   ...

If you write the rule as addition, it keeps changing:

1 ⟶ + 1 ⟹ 2 ⟶ + 2 ⟹ 4 ⟶ + 4 ⟹

You write the rule as multiplication:

1 ⟶ × 2 ⟹ 2 ⟶ × 2 ⟹ 4 ⟶ × 2 ⟹

This rule is ×**2**.

Exercise A1.1

1 ▸ Write each pattern as a number sequence.

▸ Draw the next 2 terms of each sequence.

a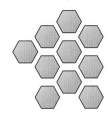

b

c

2 What are the rules for each sequence in question 1?

3 ▸ Write the rule for each of these sequences.

▸ Copy each sequence and fill in the missing terms.

The first one is done for you.

a 6, 9, **12**, 15

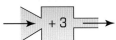

b 5, 10, 15, ___, 25

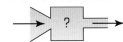

c 0.2, 0.4, 0.6, ___

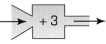

d 13, ___, 5, 1

e ⁻5, 1, ___, 13

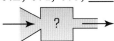

f ⁻10, ⁻4, 2, ___, 14

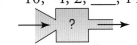

4 This bonsai tree grows to a pattern.

After year 1 it has 1 branch.

After year 2 it has 2 branches.

a Write the number of branches it has each year as a sequence. Start: 1, 2, ...

b How many branches will it have at the end of year 4?

c Write the rule for finding the number of branches the tree will have at the end of the next year.

d Explain how you know that the tree should not have an odd number of branches after year 1.

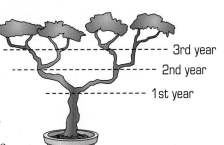

This spread will show you how to:

▶▶ Recognise and extend number sequences

KEYWORDS
Flowchart   Formula

To make a sequence you need a term-to-term rule and a start number.

This rule is add 8:

Start at 3:

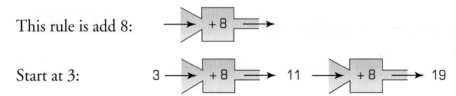

You can draw a table to show this.

3		11		19		27		35
	3 + 8		11 + 8		19 + 8		27 + 8	

This table has this rule:

The start number is 2:

2		4		8		16		32
	2 × 2		4 × 2		8 × 2		16 × 2	

This flowchart shows how to make a sequence:

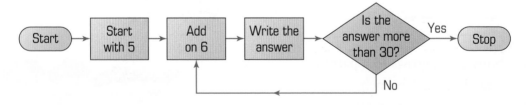

The sequence is: 5, 11, 16, 21, 26

It stops at 26, as the next term is $26 + 5 = 31$.
You stop at numbers that are more than 30.

Exercise A1.2

1 Copy and complete this table to show how to make the sequence.

The rule for the sequence is:

The sequence starts at 5.

5		11							
	5 + 6		__ + __		__ + __		__ + __		__ + __

2 Copy and complete this table to show how to make a sequence using this rule:

2									
	2 × 4		__ × __		__ × __		__ × __		__ × __

3 Draw tables to show how to make sequences with these rules and start numbers. Write 5 terms for each sequence.

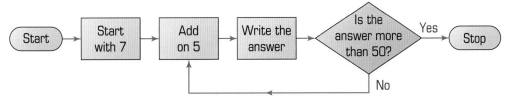

a 3 → +12 =→ Start at 3

b 29 → – 3 =→ Start at 29

c 32 → ÷ 2 =→ Start at 32

4 a Make a sequence using this flowchart.

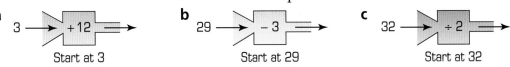

Start → Start with 7 → Add on 5 → Write the answer → Is the answer more than 50? — Yes → Stop / No

b What is the last term in this sequence?

5 a Make a sequence using this flowchart.

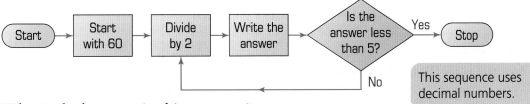

Start → Start with 60 → Divide by 2 → Write the answer → Is the answer less than 5? — Yes → Stop / No

This sequence uses decimal numbers.

b What is the last term in this sequence?

This spread will show you how to:

▶▶ Generate and describe sequences from practical contexts.
▶▶ Generate and describe simple integer sequences using position-to-term rules.
▶▶ Recognise and explain patterns and relationships.

KEYWORDS

Rule   Pattern

You can use a rule to say how many sticks you need to make each of these patterns.

Pattern 1	Pattern 2	Pattern 3
3 black + 1 red	3 black + 3 black + 1 red	3 black + 3 black + 3 black + 1 red
4 sticks	7 sticks	10 sticks

▶ The patterns go up in groups of 3 black sticks.
▶ The numbers of groups of 3 is the same as the pattern number.

   In pattern **2** there are **2** groups of 3 sticks.

▶ You always need to add 1 more for the red stick.

You can say that the number of sticks needed for any pattern is:

   ▶ Number of sticks = (pattern number × 3) + 1

To check: (Pattern number × 3) + 1

   Pattern 1: $(1 \times 3) + 1 = 4$ ✓

   Pattern 2: $(2 \times 3) + 1 = 7$ ✓

   Pattern 3: $(3 \times 3) + 1 = 10$ ✓

example

Use the rule to work out how many sticks you need for the 100th pattern.

Use the rule: (Pattern number × 3) + 1

   Pattern 100: $(100 \times 3) + 1 = 301$

You need 301 sticks.

Exercise A1.3

1 These patterns are made from matchsticks.

Pattern 1   Pattern 2   Pattern 3

   a How many burned matches are there in each pattern?
   b How many more matches are added each time?
   c How many groups of 2 matches will there be in pattern 4?
   d Copy and complete this rule:

Total number of matches = (Pattern number × __) + __

   e Use your rule to say how many matches are needed for pattern 20.

2 Here is another sequence of patterns:

  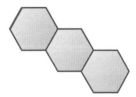

Pattern 1   Pattern 2   Pattern 3

Copy and complete these statements.
   a Pattern 1 is made from 5 blue lines and _____
   b Pattern 2 is made from __ blue lines and _____
   c Pattern 3 is made from __ blue lines and _____
   d For any pattern, the total number of lines = (Pattern number × __) + __
   e How many lines will there be altogether in pattern 10?

3 a Copy and complete the rule for this sequence of patterns:

Total number of tiles = (Pattern number × __) + __

  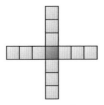

   Pattern 1   Pattern 2   Pattern 3

   b How many tiles are needed altogether for pattern 15?
   c Draw a different pattern that uses the same rule as this one.

You should know how to ...

1 Recognise and extend number sequences.

2 Generate and describe simple integer sequences.

Check out

1 Copy and continue these sequences.

   a 7, 13, 19, __, __

   b 0.5, 0.75, 1, __, __

   c 23, 20, 17, __, __

   d 10, 100, 1000, __, __

   e ⁻5, ⁻9, ⁻13, __, __

   f ⁻19, ⁻14, ⁻9, __, __

2 ▶ Write each pattern as a number sequence.

   ▶ Draw the next 2 terms of each sequence.

   ▶ Write the rule for the sequence.

   a

   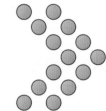

   b

   c

This unit will show you how to:

▶▶ Solve simple problems involving ratio and proportion.

▶▶ Read and plot coordinates.

▶▶ Know imperial units.

▶▶ Begin to plot and interpret graphs from real-life situations.

You can program a washing machine to carry out a function.
The results may be surprising.

Before you start

You should know how to ...

1 Use multiplication facts.

2 Read coordinates.

Check in

1 a I have 3 green counters. I have twice as many red counters.
How many red counters do I have?

   b I have 4 yellow counters for every blue counter. I have 6 blue counters. How many yellow counters do I have?

2 a Which point has the coordinates (3, 4)?

   b What are the coordinates of points A, B and C?

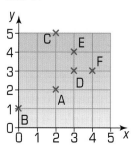

KEYWORDS

This spread will show you how to:

▶▶ Solve simple problems involving ratio and proportion.

KEYWORDS
Ratio   Proportion

There are 2 red counters for every 1 blue counter in this pattern.
The ratio of red counters to blue counters is 2 : 1

These patterns are all in the same proportion:

4 red : 2 blue   6 red : 3 blue   8 red : 4 blue

The relationship between red and blue counters in each pattern is:

▶ There are twice as many red counters as blue counters.

These patterns are not in the same proportion:

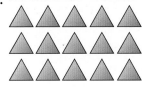

The ratio is 1 : 2   The ratio is 1 : 3   The ratio is 1 : 4

The ratio keeps changing.

example

Lucy made this pattern.
Which of these patterns are in the same proportion?

a 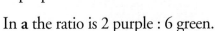   **b**   **c**

There are 3 times as many green counters as purple counters.

2 purple : 6 green

In **a** the ratio is 2 purple : 6 green.
In **b** the ratio is 1 purple : 4 green.
In **c** the ratio is 1 purple : 3 green.
Patterns **a** and **c** are in the same proportion as Lucy's pattern.

Exercise A2.1

1 What is the ratio between the yellow and red counters in each pattern?
The first one is done for you.

a Y : R
4 : 1

b

c

d

2 Which pattern in question 1 is in the same proportion as each of these patterns?
The first one is done for you.

A  Patterns **A** and **b** are proportional.
They have the same ratio, 3 : 1

B

C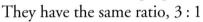

D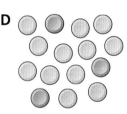

3 Which of these sets of patterns are not proportional?

a

b

c

4 Which of these price lists have proportional prices?

a

The Village Car Wash

1 token ... £3
2 tokens ... £5
3 tokens ... £8

b

Dragon Ride

1 person ... £2
10 people ... £20
20 people ... £40

c

Dry Cleaning Overnight Service

1 suit ... £6
2 suits ... £11
3 suits ... £15

This spread will show you how to:

▶▶ Solve simple problems involving ratio and proportion.
▶▶ Read and plot coordinates.

KEYWORDS
Coordinates
Proportional
Ratio

For every 1 red counter there are 2 blue counters.
The relationship between red and blue counters is proportional.

red : blue   red : blue   red : blue   red : blue
   1 : 2   2 : 4   3 : 6   4 : 8
                       1 : 2   1 : 2   1 : 2

This pattern can be drawn as a graph.

You can write the ratio as coordinates.

   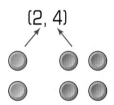

(1, 2)   (2, 4)

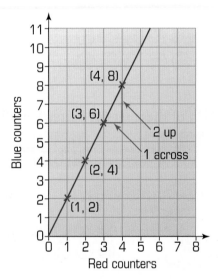

The graph line is straight because the ratio
between the numbers of red and blue counters
is always 1 : 2.
For every 1 across the graph line moves 2 up.

▶ Straight-line graphs always come from proportional
relationships.

You can extend the line
in both directions.

example

How many blue counters will there be when there are
5 red counters?

From the graph you can see that the point (5, 10) is on the line.
There are 10 blue counters when there are 5 red counters.

Exercise A2.2

1 Draw 3 sets of axes like these:

  a For each pattern, write the numbers of red and blue counters as ratios and coordinates.
  The first one is started for you.

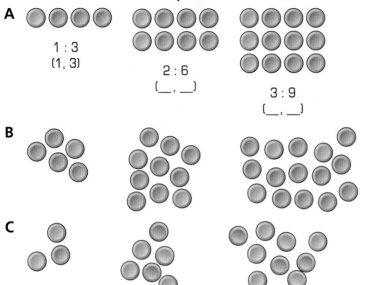

A
1 : 3
(1, 3)

2 : 6
(_ , _)

3 : 9
(_ , _)

B

C

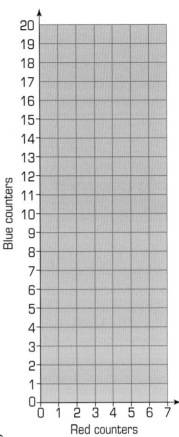

  b Plot each set of coordinates onto the axes.
  Make sure that the lines all go through (0, 0).
  c To which pattern and line does the point (5, 20) belong?

2 Which of these lines does not show a proportional relationship?
Explain how you know. You can start:
'Line ___ is not proportional because _____.'

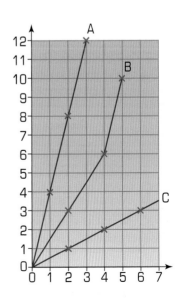

3 The fares for the Ghost Train are proportional.
  a Copy and complete the list of fares.
  b Write the number of people and the fares as coordinates.
  c Plot the coordinates on axes like those in question 1 to draw a graph of the price list.
  d Extend your graph to find out how much it costs for 6 people.

Ghost Train

1 person ... £5

3 people ... £__

5 people ... £__

This spread will show you how to:

▶▶ Read and plot coordinates.
▶▶ Know imperial units.
▶▶ Begin to plot and interpret graphs from real-life situations.

KEYWORDS
Distance　　Time
Data　　　　Speed

This table shows the distances and times of a cyclist during a race.

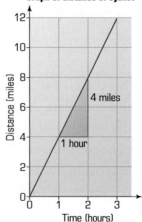

Time (hours)	0	1	2	3	4
Distance (miles)	0	15	30	45	60

You can plot the data from the table as coordinates on these axes.

The ratio between the distance he travels and the time he takes is 15 : 1.

His speed is 15 miles per hour.

▶ Speed = distance travelled in 1 hour.

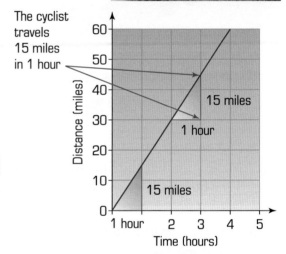

The cyclist travels 15 miles in 1 hour

example

a　Plot the data from this table as coordinates.

Distance of cyclist in a race

Time (hours)	0	1	2	3
Distance (miles)	0	4	8	12

b　What is the ratio of distance to time?
c　What is the speed of the cyclist?

a　**Graph of distance of cyclist**

b　The ratio distance : time is 4 : 1.
c　His speed is 4 miles per hour.

Exercise A2.3

1 Plot the data from the tables as coordinates on axes like these.

a

Time (hours)	0	1	2	3	4
Distance (miles)	0	10	20	60	80

b

Time (hours)	0	2	4	6
Distance (miles)	0	50	100	150

c What is the ratio of distance to time for each graph?

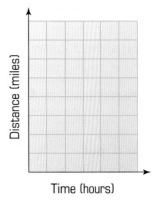

Distance (miles)

Time (hours)

2 What are the speeds shown by each graph in question 1?
Copy and complete:
a The speed is ___ miles per hour.
b The speed is ___ miles per hour.

3 This is a simplified map of the London marathon route.
It is not drawn to scale.

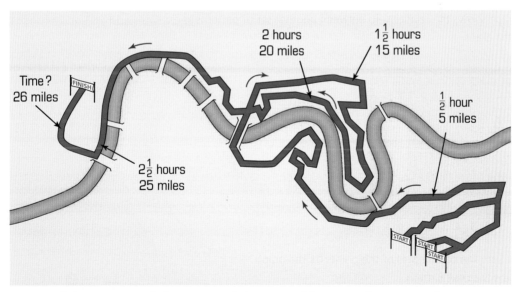

2 hours
20 miles

1½ hours
15 miles

Time?
26 miles

½ hour
5 miles

2½ hours
25 miles

FINISH

START START START

Some of the times and distances of the top athlete are shown on the map.
a Copy and complete this data table for the athlete.

Time (hours)	0	$\frac{1}{2}$	$1\frac{1}{2}$	2	$2\frac{1}{2}$
Distance (miles)					

b Draw a distance–time graph to show the data.
c Explain how you know that the athlete ran at a fairly steady speed.

You should know how to ...

1 Solve simple problems involving ratio and proportion.

2 Read and plot coordinates.

Check out

1 Which of these sets of patterns are proportional?
If the set is proportional, what is the ratio?

a

b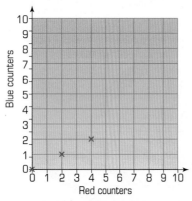

2 This graph shows the relationship between another set of patterns.
Copy the graph.

a What are the coordinates of the points on the graph?

b Here is the next pattern.
What are the coordinates for this pattern?
Plot the coordinates on your graph and join your points with a line.

c How do you know that the patterns are proportional?

d Is the point (5, 10) on your line?

e How many blue counters will you have when you have 8 red counters?

Proportional reasoning

This unit will show you how to:

- ⏩ Identify and understand equivalent fractions.
- ⏩ Reduce a fraction to its simplest form by cancelling.
- ⏩ Add and subtract fractions with the same denominator.
- ⏩ Order fractions by converting them to fractions with a common denominator.
- ⏩ Use a fraction as an operator to find fractions of numbers or quantities.
- ⏩ Recognise multiples.

- ⏩ Understand percentage as the number of parts in every 100.
- ⏩ Find simple percentages of whole-number quantities.
- ⏩ Express fractions as percentages.
- ⏩ Calculate simple percentages.
- ⏩ Reduce a ratio to its simplest form by cancelling.
- ⏩ Solve simple problems involving ratio and proportion.
- ⏩ Divide a quantity in a given ratio.

I must have got the proportions wrong!

You have to keep the right proportions to get the right results.

Before you start

You should know how to ...

1 Multiply two numbers up to 10 × 10 and use the related division facts.

2 Write a number as a fraction of another.

3 Order numbers on a number line.

Check in

1 Work out:
   a 7 × 8   **b** 6 × 3   **c** 72 ÷ 9   **d** 64 ÷ 8

2 **a** What fraction of 12 is 1?
   b What fraction of 5 is 2?
   c What fraction of 7 is 3?

3 Use a number line to order each of these sets of numbers. Start with the smallest.
   a 3, 6, 4, $3\frac{1}{2}$, 5
   b $3\frac{3}{4}$, $4\frac{1}{2}$, $2\frac{1}{4}$, $\frac{3}{4}$, $3\frac{1}{4}$

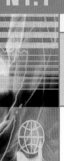

This spread will show you how to:

▶▶ Identify and understand equivalent fractions.
▶▶ Reduce a fraction to its simplest form by cancelling.

KEYWORDS
Equivalent
Fraction
Proportional
Numerator
Denominator
Cancel
Simplest form

The same fraction can be written in different ways.

| $\frac{1}{3}$ | $\frac{1}{3}$ | $\frac{1}{3}$ |

| $\frac{1}{6}$ | $\frac{1}{6}$ | $\frac{1}{6}$ |
| $\frac{1}{6}$ | $\frac{1}{6}$ | $\frac{1}{6}$ |

$\frac{1}{3}$ and $\frac{2}{6}$ are exactly the same.
They are equivalent fractions.

The blue line shows the fractions, $\frac{1}{3}$ and $\frac{2}{6}$ as
coordinates (1, 3) and (2, 6).

The coordinates are proportional because they
are on the same straight line.

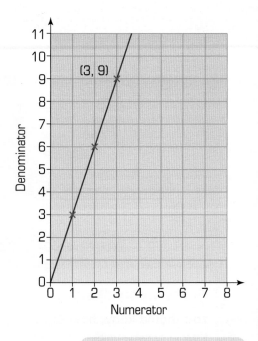

	numerator	denominator
	1	3
	2	6
	3	9

$\times 3 (\times 2 ($ ... $) \times 2) \times 3$

The coordinates (3, 9) are also on the blue line.

$\frac{3}{9}$, $\frac{1}{3}$ and $\frac{2}{6}$ are all equivalent to each other.

You can multiply and divide to find equivalent
fractions:

$$\frac{1}{3} \overset{\times 5}{=} \frac{5}{15} \qquad \frac{3}{6} \overset{\div 3}{=} \frac{1}{2} \qquad \frac{5}{15} \overset{\div 5}{=} \frac{1}{3}$$

$\times 5 \qquad\qquad \div 3 \qquad\qquad \div 5$

Remember to multiply or
divide the top and bottom
by the same number.

When you cannot cancel a fraction any further it is in
its simplest form.

$$\frac{30}{60} \overset{\div 10}{=} \frac{3}{6} \overset{\div 3}{=} \frac{1}{2}$$

$\div 10 \qquad\qquad \div 3$

Exercise N1.1

1 Write other fractions that are equivalent to a half.
Use these diagrams where 1 half ($\frac{1}{2}$) has been shaded.

a $\frac{1}{2} = \frac{?}{6}$ **b** $\frac{1}{2} = \frac{?}{10}$ **c** $\frac{1}{2} =$ **d** $\frac{1}{2} =$

2 The lines **x**, **y**, and **z** represent 3 different sets of equivalent fractions.

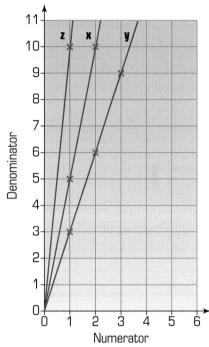

a Complete this set of fractions for line **y**.

$$\frac{1}{3} = \frac{2}{?} = \frac{?}{9}$$

b Write equivalent fractions for line **x**.

c What fraction is represented by line **z**?

d Write some fractions that are equivalent to $\frac{1}{10}$.

3 Write 3 coordinates you could plot for each of these fractions.

a $\frac{1}{4}$ **b** $\frac{1}{6}$ **c** $\frac{1}{5}$ **d** $\frac{2}{5}$ **e** $\frac{3}{5}$

4 Calculate the missing numbers in these pairs.

a $\times 5 \left(\dfrac{1 \mid 4}{5 \mid ?} \right) \times 5$ **b** $\times 2 \left(\dfrac{2 \mid 5}{4 \mid ?} \right) \times 2$ **c** $\left(\dfrac{3 \mid 7}{6 \mid ?} \right)$ **d** $\left(\dfrac{2 \mid 9}{10 \mid ?} \right)$

5 Use pairs like those in question 4 to write some equivalent fractions to these.

a $\frac{1}{6} = \frac{?}{?}$ **b** $\frac{3}{10} =$ **c** $\frac{4}{5} =$ **d** $\frac{3}{4} =$ **e** $\frac{2}{3} =$ **f** $\frac{1}{7} =$

6 Simplify each of these fractions to one of the simplest form fractions in the box:

$$\frac{1}{2} \quad \frac{1}{3} \quad \frac{1}{4} \quad \frac{2}{3} \quad \frac{3}{4}$$

a $\frac{5}{10}$ **b** $\frac{6}{9}$ **c** $\frac{3}{9}$ **d** $\frac{4}{16}$ **e** $\frac{8}{32}$ **f** $\frac{9}{18}$

g $\frac{12}{16}$ **h** $\frac{5}{15}$ **i** $\frac{27}{36}$ **j** $\frac{15}{45}$ **k** $\frac{100}{400}$ **l** $\frac{16}{24}$

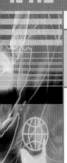

This spread will show you how to:

▶▶ Add and subtract fractions with the same denominators.

KEYWORDS
Numerator
Denominator

The cake has been divided into 8 equal pieces.
Each piece is $\frac{1}{8}$ of the cake.

3 pieces are taken out of the cake.
This is $\frac{3}{8}$ of the whole cake.
When you add the fractions, you only add
the numerators.

$$\frac{1}{8} + \frac{1}{8} + \frac{1}{8} = \frac{3}{8}$$

The whole cake is $\frac{8}{8}$ (eight eighths).

When you take away $\frac{3}{8}$ there is $\frac{5}{8}$ of the cake left.

$$\frac{8}{8} - \frac{3}{8} = \frac{5}{8}$$

This picture shows that:

$$\frac{5}{8} + \frac{2}{8} = \frac{7}{8}$$

When you add and subtract fractions:

▶ you add or subtract the numerators.

$$\frac{2}{10} + \frac{7}{10} = \frac{9}{10}$$

$$\frac{9}{10} - \frac{2}{10} = \frac{7}{10}$$

Do not add or subtract the
denominators.

Exercise N1.2

1 Write these whole numbers as fractions.
The first one is done for you.

a $1 = \frac{10}{10}$

b $1 = \frac{?}{6}$ **c** $1 = \frac{?}{20}$ **d** $1 = \frac{?}{3}$

e $1 = \frac{5}{?}$ **f** $\frac{7}{7} = \frac{14}{?}$ **g** $\frac{20}{20} = \frac{?}{5}$

2 Use the idea in question 1 to work out these subtractions.

a $1 - \frac{1}{10}$ **b** $1 - \frac{1}{5}$ **c** $1 - \frac{1}{4}$ **d** $1 - \frac{1}{7}$ **e** $1 - \frac{1}{20}$

f $1 - \frac{2}{3}$ **g** $1 - \frac{3}{4}$ **h** $1 - \frac{3}{5}$ **i** $1 - \frac{5}{9}$ **j** $1 - \frac{9}{10}$

3 Add these fractions. The first one is done for you.

a $\frac{4}{6} + \frac{1}{6} = \frac{5}{6}$

b $\frac{1}{3} + \frac{1}{3} =$ **c** $\frac{3}{8} + \frac{4}{8} =$ **d** $\frac{2}{5} + \frac{1}{5} =$ **e** $\frac{2}{9} + \frac{5}{9} =$

f $\frac{3}{20} + \frac{14}{20} =$ **g** $\frac{4}{7} + \frac{2}{7} =$ **h** $\frac{1}{10} + \frac{9}{10} =$

> Think about your answer!

4 Which of these calculations have answers that are exactly 1 whole?

a $\frac{2}{5} + \frac{3}{5}$ **b** $\frac{2}{4} + \frac{1}{4}$ **c** $\frac{2}{3} + \frac{1}{3}$ **d** $\frac{1}{7} + \frac{5}{7}$

5 a $\frac{2}{10}$ and $\frac{5}{10}$ of this rectangle have been shaded.
What fraction of the rectangle is shaded altogether?

$\frac{1}{10}$	$\frac{1}{10}$	$\frac{1}{10}$	$\frac{1}{10}$	$\frac{1}{10}$
$\frac{1}{10}$	$\frac{1}{10}$	$\frac{1}{10}$	$\frac{1}{10}$	$\frac{1}{10}$

b Draw a rectangle like this and divide it into 10 equal parts.
By shading, show this calculation: $\frac{3}{10} + \frac{6}{10}$

c What fraction do you need to shade so that the whole rectangle is shaded?

6 a Jake does $\frac{3}{5}$ of his homework in school.
How much has he to do at home?

b Lauren uses $\frac{5}{6}$ of her lipstick in one go.
What fraction of her lipstick is left?

This spread will show you how to:

▸▸ Order fractions by converting them to fractions with a common denominator
▸▸ Position fractions on a number line.
▸▸ Represent problems mathematically.

KEYWORDS

Equivalent
Mixed number
Denominator
Greater than (>)
Less than (<)

When you are comparing fractions that have different denominators, you need to use equivalent fractions.

These fractions have different denominators.

| $\frac{1}{2}$ |
| $\frac{1}{2}$ |

| $\frac{1}{3}$ | $\frac{1}{3}$ | $\frac{1}{3}$ |

You change both fractions so that they have the same denominator.

| $\frac{1}{6}$ | $\frac{1}{6}$ | $\frac{1}{6}$ |
| $\frac{1}{6}$ | $\frac{1}{6}$ | $\frac{1}{6}$ |

| $\frac{1}{6}$ | $\frac{1}{6}$ | $\frac{1}{6}$ |
| $\frac{1}{6}$ | $\frac{1}{6}$ | $\frac{1}{6}$ |

$\frac{1}{2}$ is equivalent to $\frac{3}{6}$ $\frac{1}{3}$ is equivalent to $\frac{2}{6}$

$\frac{3}{6}$ is greater than $\frac{2}{6}$

so $\frac{1}{2}$ is greater than $\frac{1}{3}$

On a number line:

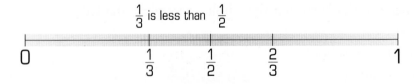

$\frac{1}{3}$ is less than $\frac{1}{2}$

You can write this as:
$\frac{1}{3} < \frac{1}{2}$

▸ $2\frac{1}{2}$ is a mixed number.

You can change it into a fraction like this:
$2\frac{1}{2} = 1 + 1 + \frac{1}{2} = \frac{2}{2} + \frac{2}{2} + \frac{1}{2} = \frac{5}{2}$

▸ $\frac{5}{2}$ is an improper or top heavy fraction.

Exercise N1.3

Sometimes you see fractions and whole numbers together.

1 Use the drawings to decide if these statements are true.

a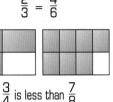

$\frac{2}{3} = \frac{4}{6}$

b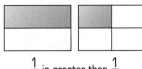

$\frac{1}{2}$ is greater than $\frac{1}{4}$

c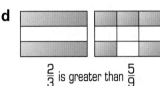

$\frac{3}{4}$ is less than $\frac{7}{8}$

d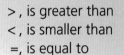

$\frac{2}{3}$ is greater than $\frac{5}{9}$

2 Use the drawings in question 1 to help you copy and complete these statements.

Fill each blank with a symbol from the box.

> >, is greater than
> <, is smaller than
> =, is equal to

a $\frac{1}{6}$ ___ $\frac{2}{3}$ (drawing **a**)   **b** $\frac{3}{8}$ ___ $\frac{1}{4}$ (drawing **c**)

c $\frac{1}{3}$ ___ $\frac{2}{9}$ (drawing **d**)   **d** $\frac{1}{2}$ ___ $\frac{1}{4}$ (drawing **b**)

e $\frac{2}{3}$ ___ $\frac{1}{9}$ (drawing **d**)   **f** $\frac{5}{8}$ ___ $\frac{1}{4}$ (drawing **c**)

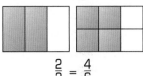

3 Use this number line to copy and complete these statements.

a $\frac{3}{8}$ ___ $\frac{1}{2}$ **b** $\frac{3}{4}$ ___ $\frac{1}{8}$ **c** $\frac{5}{8}$ ___ $\frac{3}{4}$ **d** $\frac{1}{4}$ ___ $\frac{2}{8}$

4 Draw number lines to help you copy and complete each of these statements.

a $\frac{1}{3}$ ___ $\frac{3}{6}$ **b** $\frac{2}{10}$ ___ $\frac{1}{5}$ **c** $\frac{1}{4}$ ___ $\frac{4}{20}$ **d** $\frac{2}{3}$ ___ $\frac{7}{9}$

e $\frac{4}{5}$ ___ $\frac{1}{2}$ **f** $\frac{3}{4}$ ___ $\frac{2}{5}$ **g** $\frac{2}{3}$ ___ $\frac{5}{8}$ **h** $\frac{1}{4}$ ___ $\frac{3}{7}$

5 Change each of these mixed numbers into simple fractions.

a $1\frac{1}{2}$ **b** $1\frac{1}{3}$ **c** $1\frac{3}{4}$ **d** $1\frac{5}{6}$ **e** $1\frac{1}{8}$ **f** $2\frac{1}{3}$

g $2\frac{1}{2}$ **h** $3\frac{1}{4}$ **i** $2\frac{7}{8}$ **j** $2\frac{5}{9}$ **k** $2\frac{1}{10}$ **l** $3\frac{5}{7}$

6 Change these top heavy fractions into mixed numbers.

a $\frac{6}{5}$ **b** $\frac{7}{4}$ **c** $\frac{9}{2}$ **d** $\frac{11}{3}$ **e** $\frac{16}{5}$ **f** $\frac{21}{5}$

This spread will show you how to:

▶▶ Use a fraction as an operator to find fractions of numbers or quantities.

KEYWORDS

Divide Denominator
Multiply Numerator

▶ To find $\frac{1}{4}$, you divide by 4.

Here are 12 CDs.

To find $\frac{1}{4}$ of them, you split them into 4 equal groups:

$$12 \div 4 = 3$$

so $\quad \frac{1}{4}$ of $12 = 3$

$\frac{3}{4}$ of $12 = 3 \times 3$

$\frac{3}{4}$ of $12 = 9$

▶ To calculate any fraction of a number, you divide by the denominator then multiply by the numerator.

example

You can use a calculator to calculate harder fractions.

The crowd at this concert was 4510 people. $\frac{4}{5}$ of the crowd were less than 25 years old. How many people were less than 25?

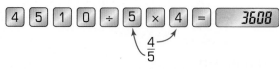

3608 people were less than 25.

Exercise N1.4

1 $\frac{1}{3}$ of these counters have been circled.
How many counters is $\frac{2}{3}$ of the total?

2 Calculate $\frac{3}{4}$ of these tiles.

3 Work out these fractions of amounts.
  a $\frac{1}{4}$ of 20 CDs   **b** $\frac{1}{5}$ of £20   **c** $\frac{1}{3}$ of 60 cm
  d $\frac{1}{6}$ of 30 apples   **e** $\frac{1}{10}$ of €90   **f** $\frac{1}{8}$ of 24 mm

4 These bricks are $\frac{1}{10}$ of the total needed to make a small garden wall.
How many bricks are there altogether in the wall?

5 Copy and complete these sentences.
  a When you calculate $\frac{1}{4}$ of a number you divide by ____
  b When you calculate $\frac{1}{5}$ of a number you divide by ____
  c When you calculate $\frac{1}{10}$ of a number you _____ by ____

6 Calculate these fractions of amounts.
  a $\frac{2}{3}$ of £30   **b** $\frac{4}{5}$ of 15 kg   **c** $\frac{3}{10}$ of 20 mm   **d** $\frac{2}{7}$ of 21 students
  e $\frac{3}{5}$ of £60   **f** $\frac{7}{10}$ of €50   **g** $\frac{5}{6}$ of 30 m   **h** $\frac{3}{8}$ of 16 tonnes

7 The attendance at this football game was 28 800 people.

$\frac{3}{4}$ of the fans supported the home side.
  a How many home side fans attended?
  b How many fans supported the away side?
  c How can you check your answer without doing the same calculation again?

This spread will show you how to:

▶▶ Understand percentage as the number of parts in every 100.
▶▶ Find simple percentages of whole-number quantities.

KEYWORDS
Percentage
Equivalent
Decimal

▶ A percentage is a fraction out of 100: 37% is $\frac{37}{100}$.

10% is the same as $\frac{10}{100}$. $\frac{10}{100}$ is equivalent to $\frac{1}{10}$.

▶ To find 10% or $\frac{1}{10}$, you divide by 10.

example

There is £20 in pound coins in this pile. Find 10% of the money.

Divide the coins into 10 equal piles:

10% 10% 10% 10% 10%

10% 10% 10% 10% 10%

So, 10% of £20 is £2 because
£20 ÷ 10 = £2.

▶ 20% is 2 × 10%
▶ 30% is 3 × 10%

10% of £20 is £2 so,   **20% of £20 is 2 × £2 = £4**

10% 10%

30% of £20 is 3 × £2 = £6.

10% 10% 10%

Some calculations have decimal answers.

example

There are 15 pound coins in this pile. Find 10% of the money.

When you divide by 10 you move the digits 1 place to the right.

$$t \quad u \;.\; \tfrac{1}{10} \;\; \tfrac{1}{100}$$

$$1 \quad 5 \;.\; 0 \qquad \div 10$$

$$1 \;.\; 5 \quad 0$$

So 10% of £15 = £1.50

Exercise N1.5

1 What percentage of these grids are orange?

a 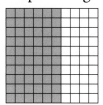   **b** 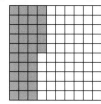   **c**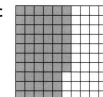

2 Write these percentages as fractions.

  a 29%   **b** 39%   **c** 43%   **d** 73%   **e** 99%

3 Calculate 10% of these amounts.

  a 50 kg   **b** 60 cm   **c** 90 km   **d** 70 mm   **e** £100
  f €120   **g** 150 cm   **h** 170 people   **i** £190   **j** £200

4 This ruler is 20 cm long.

  a If you snapped off 10% of the ruler
  how long would that piece be?

  b How long would the larger piece be?

5 Here are 50 pound coins.

  a How much is 10% of the money?

  b How much is 30% of the money?

6 Calculate 10% of £25.

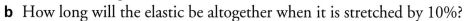

7 a Calculate 10% of £55.

  b How much is 20% of £55?

8 An elastic band is 80 mm long.

  a If the elastic is stretched by 10%
  how much longer will it be?

  b How long will the elastic be altogether when it is stretched by 10%?

  c The elastic band can be stretched by 60% before it snaps.
  How long is 60% of the original length?

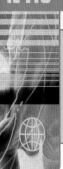

This spread will show you how to:
- ▶▶ Understand percentage as the number of parts in every 100.
- ▶▶ Express fractions as percentages.
- ▶▶ Calculate simple percentages.

KEYWORDS

Percent

All percentages can be written as fractions 'out of one hundred'.

20% means $\frac{20}{100}$

$\frac{20}{100}$ means $20 \div 100$

example

Change these fractions to percentages.

a $\frac{19}{100}$ **b** $\frac{3}{10}$ **c** $\frac{1}{2}$ **d** $\frac{3}{4}$

a A percentage is a fraction out of 100.

$\frac{19}{100} = 19\%$

b You need to find an equivalent fraction with a denominator of 100.

$$\frac{3}{10} \xrightarrow{\times 10} = \frac{30}{100} = 30\%$$

c

$$\frac{1}{2} \xrightarrow{50} = \frac{50}{100} = 50\%$$

d

$$\frac{3}{4} \xrightarrow{25} = \frac{75}{100} = 75\%$$

You can use a calculator to work out percentages of an amount.

example

Find 15% of £73.

Sale 15% off
Was £73

15% means $\frac{15}{100}$ or $15 \div 100$

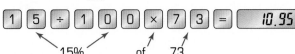

$$\boxed{1}\,\boxed{5}\,\boxed{\div}\,\boxed{1}\,\boxed{0}\,\boxed{0}\,\boxed{\times}\,\boxed{7}\,\boxed{3}\,\boxed{=}\quad \boxed{10.95}$$

15%   of   73

Calculators do not show units, so you must remember that your answer is in money.

15% of £73 = £10·95

Exercise N1.6

1 Write these percentages as fractions.

a $21\% = \frac{?}{100}$ **b** $9\% = \frac{?}{100}$ **c** $17\% =$ **d** $7\% =$ **e** $13\% =$

f $23\% =$ **g** $39\% =$ **h** $43\% =$ **i** $67\% =$ **j** $99\% =$

2 Change these fractions to percentages.

a $\frac{3}{100}$ **b** $\frac{5}{100}$ **c** $\frac{19}{100}$ **d** $\frac{80}{100}$ **e** $\frac{77}{100}$

f $\frac{25}{100}$ **g** $\frac{45}{100}$ **h** $\frac{63}{100}$ **i** $\frac{59}{100}$ **j** $\frac{100}{100}$

3 Change these fractions to percentages.

a $\frac{3}{10}$ **b** $\frac{9}{10}$ **c** $\frac{1}{50}$ **d** $\frac{3}{50}$ **e** $\frac{17}{50}$

f $\frac{1}{25}$ **g** $\frac{8}{25}$ **h** $\frac{1}{2}$ **i** $\frac{1}{4}$ **j** $\frac{1}{5}$

4 These buttons show how you would work out 45% of £300 on your calculator.

a Copy the calculation and fill in the missing buttons.

b What is 45% of £300?

5 Use your calculator to work out these percentages of amounts.

a 65% of £90 = £   **b** 24% of 75 kg   **c** 8% of £96

d 15% of £60   **e** 35% of €10   **f** 65% of 15 cm

6 a Use your calculator to work out: **i** 40% of £400.

                                    ii 60% of £400.

b How can you check your answers without doing the same calculations twice?

7 James drives from Kingston to Oxford. The journey is 55 miles.

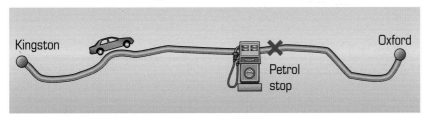

a Estimate the percentage of the distance travelled when James stopped for petrol.

b Use your calculator to calculate these distances.

   i 60% of 55 miles   **ii** 15% of 55 miles   **iii** 45% of 55 miles

This spread will show you how to:

▶▶ Reduce a ratio to its simplest form by cancelling.
▶▶ Solve simple problems involving ratio and proportion.

KEYWORDS
Simplest form
Factor   Ratio   Simplify

There are different ways to look at this picture.

You could say that:

▶ there are 12 dogs and 4 owners
▶ there are 3 dogs for every 1 owner
▶ there is 1 owner for every 3 dogs.

You can write the relationship between dogs and owners as a ratio.

dogs : owners
12 : 4

You can write the ratio in its simplest form.

dogs : owners
3 : 1

The factor that connects the ratios is 4.
You divide by 4 to simplify.

	dogs	owners	
÷4 (	12	4	) ÷4
	3	1	

---

example

The ratio of dogs to owners is 3 :1.
There are 15 dogs. How many owners are there?

....

	dogs	owners	
×5 (	3	1	) ×5
	15	5	

There are 5 owners.

Exercise N1.7

1 For each drawing, write the ratio of red to blue beads. Use the : sign.

 **a**   **b**    **c**

d

e

f

2 Write the ratios in question 1 in their simplest form.

3 Use these tables to help you write these ratios in their simplest form.
Each question has been started for you.

a 5 : 15   **b** 8 : 16   **c** 9 : 3   **d** 25 : 5

5	15
1	?

8	16
1	?

9	3
?	1

25	5
?	1

e 18 : 9   **f** 12 : 18   **g** 16 : 24   **h** 16 : 40

18	9
2	?

12	18
?	3

16	24
2	?

16	40
2	?

4 Write these ratios in their simplest form.

   a 6 : 18   **b** 14 : 7   **c** 15 : 30   **d** 100 : 25

   e 6 : 9   **f** 15 : 10   **g** 14 : 21   **h** 9 : 12

5 a James and Liz pick blackberries.
James collects 50 berries and Liz picks 70 berries.
Write the ratio of James' collection to Liz's
collection in its simplest form.

James	Liz
50	70

   b How many berries would you expect Liz to
pick if James picked 150?

	James	Liz
×?	50	70
	150		×?

6 A very strong glue is made from a resin and a hardener.
They are mixed in the ratio 3 : 2.
If you use 45 grams of resin, how many grams of hardener
will you need?

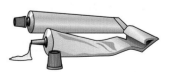

This spread will show you how to:

▶▶ Divide a quantity in a given ratio.

Karis and Donna wash car windscreens on Saturdays.
One Saturday they earned £15.

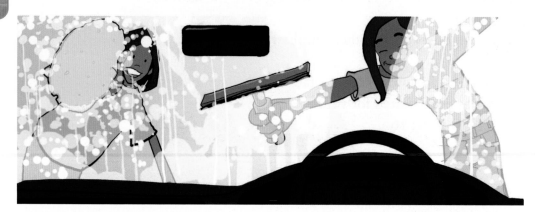

Donna washed 3 screens and Karis washed 2.
They divide the money in the ratio 3 : 2.

For every £3 that Donna receives, Karis receives £2.

Karis : Donna

£2 : £3 → £5

£4 : £6 → £10   Go up in £5s because the ratio 3 : 2 adds to 5.

£6 : £9 → £15

Karis receives £6 and Donna receives £9.

---

example

Share out £21 in the ratio 6 : 1.

6 : 1 → £7

12 : 2 → £14   Go up in £7s because the ratio 6 : 1 adds to 7.

18 : 3 → £21

£21 shared in the ratio 6 : 1 is £18 and £3.
Check: £18 + £3 = £21 ✓

Exercise N1.8

1 Divide £20 in the ratio 2 : 3. The answer has been started for you.

$\longrightarrow$ £5

$\longrightarrow$ £10

$\longrightarrow$

2 Emily and Josh share 18 sweets. They share them in the ratio 2 : 1.
They start like this.

Emily : Josh

How many sweets does each person receive?

3 Graham mixes blue and yellow paints in the ratio 1 : 3 to make green.
If he has 3 tins of blue paint, how many tins of yellow paint will he need?

4 Can Jamilla share out 25 counters in this ratio?

1 : 3

Explain your answer.

5 Steve mixes red and black paint to make 28 litres of brown paint.
He uses the ratio   Red : Black
              3 : 4

How many litres of each colour does Steve use?

6 Sarah and Martin are collecting names for a school meal petition.
Sarah collects 4 names for every 1 name that Martin collects.
  a Write this as a ratio.   Sarah : Martin =
  b How many names does each one collect if they collect 30 names altogether?

7 Share £24 in the ratio of 3 : 5.

This spread will show you how to:

▸▸ Solve simple problems involving ratio and proportion.
▸▸ Recognise multiples.

KEYWORDS
Factor

Here is a recipe for vanilla ice cream.
The recipe is for 2 people.

Ingredients

1 egg
250 ml milk
125 ml cream
1 vanilla pod
40 g sugar

To make the same ice cream for 6
people you use 3 times the ingredients.
The multiplication factor is 3.

	Eggs	Milk	Cream	Vanilla	Sugar
2 people	1	250 mℓ	125 mℓ	1 pod	40 g
6 people	③× 1 = 3 eggs	③× 250 = 750 mℓ	③× 125 = 375 mℓ	③× 1 = 3 pods	③× 40 = 120 g

To make the same ice cream for 10 people the multiplication
factor is 5 (5 × 2 = 10).

	Eggs	Milk	Cream	Vanilla	Sugar
2 people	1	250 mℓ	125 mℓ	1 pod	40 g
10 people	⑤× 1 = 5 eggs	⑤× 250 = 1250 mℓ	⑤× 125 = 625 mℓ	⑤× 1 = 5 pods	⑤× 40 = 200 g

example

Here is a recipe for pancake batter.
The recipe is for 4 people.
a What is the multiplication factor to make enough for 8 people?
b Re-write the recipe to make enough for 8 people.

Ingredients

2 eggs
250 ml milk
100 g flour

a The multiplication factor is 2 (2 × 4 = 8).
b

	Eggs	Flour	Milk
4 people	2	100 g	250 mℓ
8 people	2 × 2 = 4 eggs	2 × 100 = 200 g	2 × 250 = 500 mℓ

Exercise N1.9

1 Here is a recipe for scrambled eggs.
It makes enough for 3 people.

What are the multiplication factors needed to make enough for:
a 6 people   **b** 9 people   **c** 15 people   **d** 30 people

> **Ingredients**
>
> 2 eggs
> 100 ml milk
> 30 g butter
> No salt!

2 Re-write the recipe in question 1 to make enough for 12 people.
Use this table to help you.

	Eggs	Milk	Butter
3 people	2	200 mℓ	30 g
12 people			

3 Zak is painting the rooms in a hotel with purple paint.
He mixes 4 litres of blue paint with 6 litres of red paint.
There is enough for 1 room.

a Copy and complete the table to show how much paint
he will use to paint:

  ▸ 5 rooms
  ▸ 7 rooms
  ▸ 10 rooms.

	Red	Blue
1 room	4	6
5 rooms	?	?
7 rooms	?	?
10 rooms	?	?

b Zak needs 2 litres of red paint to paint a bathroom purple.
How much blue paint does he need?

red	blue
4	6
2	?

×? (   ) ×?

4 Rob irons for money. He irons 24 shirts in 3 hours.
a How many shirts does he iron in 1 hour?

hours	shirts
3	24
1	?

b How many shirts does he iron in 4 hours?

You should know how to ...

1 Reduce a fraction to its simplest form by cancelling.

2 Use a fraction to find fractions of numbers or quantities.

3 Understand percentage as the number of parts in every 100.

4 Find simple percentages of whole-number quantities.

5 Solve simple problems involving ratio and proportion.

Check out

1 Write these fractions in their simplest form.

  a $\frac{5}{10}$ **b** $\frac{2}{8}$

  c $\frac{3}{9}$ **d** $\frac{4}{6}$

  e $\frac{12}{16}$ **f** $\frac{18}{81}$

2 Work out:

  a $\frac{1}{2}$ of 6   **b** $\frac{1}{4}$ of 16

  c $\frac{1}{5}$ of £10   **d** $\frac{3}{4}$ of 20

  e $\frac{3}{10}$ of £30   **f** $\frac{1}{10}$ of £3

3 Write these percentages as fractions.

  a 29%

  b 33%

  c 67%

4 a Find 10% of 70 kg.

  b Find 10% of £40.

  c Find 20% of £40.

5 To make pale green paint, Jack mixes green and white paint in the ratio 2 : 5.
He uses 6 litres of green paint.
How many litres of white paint does he use?

This unit will show you how to:

▶▶ Simplify expressions by collecting like terms.

▶▶ Develop from explaining a generalised relationship in words to expressing it in a formula using letters as symbols.

▶▶ Use the relationship between the 4 operations.

▶▶ Construct and solve simple linear equations.

▶▶ Recognise square numbers to at least 12 × 12 and the corresponding roots.

In algebra, you need to balance both sides

Before you start

You should know how to ...

1 Add and subtract numbers.

2 Multiply and divide simple numbers.

Check in

1 Work out these as quickly as you can.

   a 8 + 6 − 9   **b** 10 − 7 + 5

   c 1 + 3 − 4   **d** 2 − 1 + 5

   e 10 + 8 − 1   **f** 4 − 3 − 6

   g 2 + 7 − 6 − 9   **h** 10 + 3 − 1 − 7

2 Work out these as quickly as you can.

   a 4 × 7   **b** 3 × 5

   c 6 × 8   **d** 2 × 9

   e 56 ÷ 8   **f** 90 ÷ 9

   g 18 ÷ 6   **h** 20 ÷ 4

This spread will show you how to:

▶▶ Begin to explain a generalised relationship in words as a formula using letters as symbols.
▶▶ Simplify expressions by collecting like terms.

KEYWORDS

Expression	Symbol
Like	Collect
Simplify	Like terms
Unlike terms	Represent

You can use symbols such as letters to represent numbers.
You can sort and count the symbols (letters) in the box.

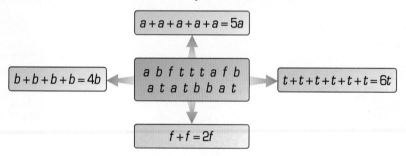

$$a + a + a + a + a = 5a$$

$$b + b + b + b = 4b$$

a b f t t t a f b
a t a t b b a t

$$t + t + t + t + t + t = 6t$$

$$f + f = 2f$$

▶ **You can add or subtract like symbols.**

example

Simplify:
a $a + a + a + 2a$ **b** $7t + 3t - 4t$
c $6y + 2y + 5y$ **d** $10g - 5g + 2g$

....

a $a + a + a + 2a = 5a$ **b** $7t + 3t - 4t = 6t$
c $6y + 2y + 5y = 13y$ **d** $10g - 5g + 2g = 7g$

Like symbols use the same letter.
This is a letter pyramid.

a + b + a

Add the 'a' symbols
together and add the
'b' symbols together

$a + b$ + $b + a$

$a + b + b + a = 2a + 2b$

You cannot simplify $a + b$ any further because they are unlike terms.

▶ **An expression is a collection of numbers and letters without an equals sign.**
$2a + 2b$

Exercise A3.1

1 Sort the like symbols in these targets.
Simplify them by addition.

a

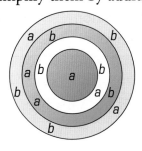

b

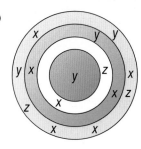

2 Copy and complete these pyramids to make simplified expressions.

a

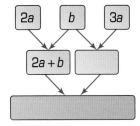

b

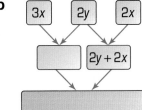

c

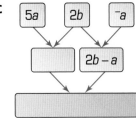

d

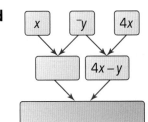

3 Connect the expressions on the left to the simplified versions on the right of this mapping.
Write each answer like this:

$$y + x + 4x \longrightarrow 5x + y$$

Expression	Simplified
$y + x + 4x$	$7x + 7y$
$5x - 2y - x + 3y$	$x + 2y$
$9x - 6x + 2y - 2x$	0
$20x - 10y - 8x$	$12x - 10y$
$x - 2x + x + x$	$2y$
$12x + 8y - 5x - y$	$4x + y$
$3x + 8x - 11x$	$5y$
$5x - 8x + 2y + 3x$	$5x + y$
$6x + 2x - x + y - x$	$6x + y$
$3x - 5x + 5y + 2x$	x

This spread will show you how to:

▶▶ Develop from explaining a generalised relationship in words to expressing it in a formula using letters as symbols.

KEYWORDS
Expression
Symbol

Inside the bag there are *n* marbles.

Outside the bag there are 5 marbles.

 +

Altogether there are *n* + 5 marbles.
n stands for the number of marbles in the bag.

n + 5 is an expression.

This bag contained *m* marbles but 3 marbles rolled out.

There are *m* − 3 marbles left in the bag.

There are *t* pins in each box.

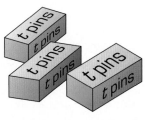

There are 3 boxes here, so there are 3 × *t* pins altogether.

You can write 3*t* instead of 3 × *t*.

example

There are *t* pins in a box.
How many pins are there in:
a 10 boxes
b 2 full boxes and 15 loose pins?

a In 4 boxes there are 4 × *t* or 4*t* pins.
b In 2 full boxes there are 2 × *t* or 2*t* pins.
Adding 15 loose pins makes 2*t* + 15 pins.

Exercise A3.2

1 Write an expression to say how many marbles there are in each picture.
Use the symbol *n* for the unknown number of marbles in each bag.

a  **b**   **c**  **d**

2 There were *m* marbles in each bag, but some marbles have rolled out.
How many marbles are left in each bag?

a **b** **c** **d**

3 There are *c* chocolates in a box.
How many chocolates are there in:

a 3 boxes
b 6 full boxes and 2 extra chocolates
c 1 box after 4 have been eaten?
d If *c* stands for 12 chocolates, how many is *c* + 6?

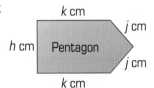

c chocolates

4 Write the shortest expression you can for the perimeters of these shapes.
1 shape has 3 different lengths and uses unlike symbols.

> Remember: Perimeter is the distance around the edge of a shape.

a

n cm
n cm   *n* cm
n cm Octagon *n* cm
n cm   *n* cm
n cm

b
x cm

Square
Sides *x* cm

c
k cm
j cm
h cm Pentagon
j cm
k cm

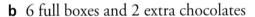

d If *n* is 5 cm, what is the perimeter of the octagon?

5 Jan and Dean are sharing their earphones.
Each of their wires is *y* cm long.
Make an expression using *y* cm for the furthest distance apart that Jan and Dean can be.

This spread will show you how to:

▶▶ Use the relationship between the 4 operations.
▶▶ Express a relationship in a formula using letters as symbols.
▶▶ Construct and solve simple linear equations.

KEYWORDS

Inverse operation
Solve
Equation

▶ An inverse operation gets you back to where you started.

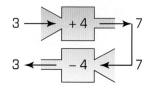

$3 + 4 = 7$

The inverse operation is subtract 4:

$7 - 4 = 3$

$5 \times 7 = 35$

The inverse operation is divide by 7:

$35 \div 7 = 5$

You can use inverse operations to solve problems.

example

There is some money in this wallet and there are 13 loose pound coins.

Altogether there is £28.

How much money is in the wallet?

Use the symbol n to represent the money in the wallet.

The equation is: $n + 13 = 28$

Use an inverse operation to calculate the amount of money in the wallet.

$n = £15$, so there is £15 in the wallet.

Check: $13 + 15 = 28$

Exercise A3.3

1 What are the inverses of these operations?

a  × 5

b + 10

c ÷ 8

2 Use inverse operations to calculate the input numbers in each question.
The first one has been started for you.

a ? → × 3 → 24
? ← ÷ 3 ←

b ? → ÷ 5 → 40

c ? → − 10 → 70

d ? → × 7 → 28

e ? → ÷ 9 → 3

f ? → + 15 → 41

3 Match each equation with its function machine.

a $x + 21 = 7$

A x → ÷ 7 → 3

b $x - 21 = 7$

B x → − 21 → 7

c $3x = 21$

C x → + 21 → 7

d $\frac{x}{7} = 3$

D x → × 3 → 21

4 Katie has some money in her wallet. She also has £9 in coins.
When she counts up all her money she has £34.

a Complete this diagram to calculate the money in Katie's wallet.

x → ? → 34
? ← ? ← 34

b If Katie has 5 notes in her wallet, how much is each note worth?

5 Calculate the values of the symbols in each of these equations.

a $x + 15 = 23$ **b** $y - 11 = 9$ **c** $m \div 5 = 4$ **d** $\frac{x}{10} = 5$

6 a Change this 'story' into an equation.
  b Solve the equation to find Donna's weight
    before her diet.

> *Donna lost 11 kg on her diet.*
> *Now she weighs 47 kg.*

This spread will show you how to:

▶▶ Use the relationship between the 4 operations.
▶▶ Express a relationship in a formula using letters as symbols.
▶▶ Construct and solve simple linear equations.

KEYWORDS

Inverse   Solve
Input   Output
Operation
Function machine

This function machine has 2 operations.
Multiply the input by 2 → Subtract 3 from the answer

$$(10 \times 2 = 20) \quad (20 - 3 = 17)$$

$$10 \longrightarrow \boxed{\times 2} \longrightarrow 20 \longrightarrow \boxed{-3} \longrightarrow 17$$

To calculate the input, you use the inverse operations.
▶ Write the inverse of each function.
▶ Work through the function machine in the reverse order.

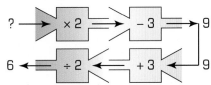

The inverse of ×**2** is ÷**2** and the inverse of −**3** is +**3**.

$$12 \div 2 = 6 \qquad 9 + 3 = 12$$

The input was 6.

To check your answer, use 6 as the input in the original function machine. You get an output of 9.

example

The perimeter of this triangle is 26 cm.
What is x?

x cm   △   *x* cm
10 cm

The perimeter is $x + x + 10$ cm $= 2x + 10$ cm.
So $2x + 10 = 26$.
Use inverse operations to solve this equation.

$$x \longrightarrow \boxed{\times 2} \longrightarrow \boxed{+ 10} \longrightarrow 26$$
$$8 \longleftarrow \boxed{\div 2} \longleftarrow \boxed{- 10} \longleftarrow 26$$

The output is 8, so the distance
x is 8 cm.

Check your answer by using 8 as the input in the original function machine.

$$8 \longrightarrow \boxed{\times 2} \longrightarrow 16 \longrightarrow \boxed{+ 10} \longrightarrow 26$$

Exercise A3.4

1 Calculate the outputs from these machines.

a
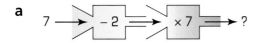
7 → □ – 2 → □ × 7 → ?

b
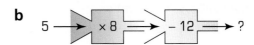
5 → □ × 8 → □ – 12 → ?

c
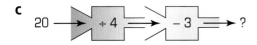
20 → □ ÷ 4 → □ – 3 → ?

d
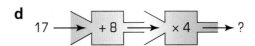
17 → □ + 8 → □ × 4 → ?

2 ▸ Copy and complete the diagrams by writing the inverse of each operation.
  ▸ Calculate the input of each of the 2-step machines.
The first one has been started for you.

a
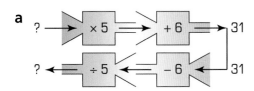
? → □ × 5 → □ + 6 → 31
? ← □ ÷ 5 ← □ – 6 ← 31

b
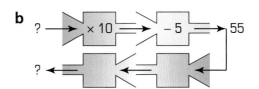
? → □ × 10 → □ – 5 → 55
? ← □ ← □ ←

c
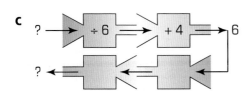
? → □ ÷ 6 → □ + 4 → 6
? ← □ ← □ ←

d
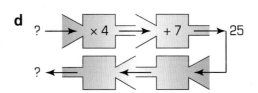
? → □ × 4 → □ + 7 → 25
? ← □ ← □ ←

3 Solve these equations to calculate the value of the symbols.
You can use 2-step function machines.

a $3x - 3 = 12$ **b** $5x + 4 = 24$ **c** $3y + 13 = 43$
d $7p - 4 = 31$ **e** $10w + 16 = 36$ **f** $8t - 3 = 21$
g $\frac{x}{5} - 2 = 10$ **h** $\frac{x}{3} + 10 = 12$ **i** $\frac{w}{9} - 2 = 0$

$\frac{x}{5}$ means $x \div 5$

4 For each shape:
  a Make a 2-step equation.
  b Solve the equation. (You can use 2-step function machines.)
    i Perimeter = 39 cm   **ii** Perimeter = 45 cm   **iii** Perimeter = 46 cm

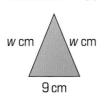
w cm   w cm
9 cm

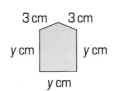
3 cm   3 cm
y cm   y cm
y cm

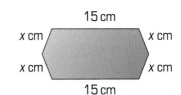
15 cm
x cm   x cm
x cm   x cm
15 cm

This spread will show you how to:

▶▶ Recognise square numbers to at least 12 × 12.

KEYWORDS

Area   cm²

Squared

Square number

A square has all 4 sides equal and all 4 angles equal.

▶ **Area of a square = length × width**

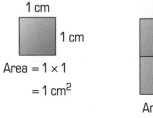

1 cm

1 cm

Area = 1 × 1

= 1 cm²

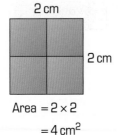

2 cm

2 cm

Area = 2 × 2

= 4 cm²

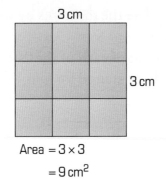

3 cm

3 cm

Area = 3 × 3

= 9 cm²

The numbers **1**, **4** and **9** are the first 3 square numbers.

You can see these square numbers on this table:

You can calculate the next square number by multiplying 4 × 4.

4 × 4 = 16

You write $4^2 = 16$.
You say '4 squared is 16'.

×	1	2	3	4
1	1	2	3	4
2	2	4	6	8
3	3	6	9	12
4	4	8	12	1

▶ **To square means to multiply a number by itself.**

Write the next 3 terms of this sequence.

1, 4, 9, 16, __, __, __

....

The terms of the sequence are the square numbers.

1 × 1 = 1   2 × 2 = 4

3 × 3 = 9   4 × 4 = 16

The next 3 terms are:

5 × 5 = 25   6 × 6 = 36   7 × 7 = 49

Exercise A3.5

1 Calculate the areas of these squares.
Do not measure them as they are not drawn to size.
The units of your answers will be cm^2.

a 3 cm

3 cm

b 4 cm
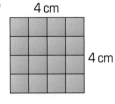
4 cm

c 5 cm
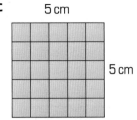
5 cm

2 Copy and complete these square number calculations up to 100.

  a 1×1 **b** 2×2 **c** 3×3 **d** 4×4 **e** 5×5

  f 6×6 **g** 7×7 **h** 8×8 **i** 9×9 **j** 10×10

3 Calculate the value of these square numbers.
You can use a calculator to help you.

  a $7^2 = 7 \times 7 = 49$

  b $11^2 = 11 \times 11 =$ **c** $12^2 = 12 \times 12 =$ **d** $25^2 = 25 \times 25 =$

  e 20^2 **f** 30^2 **g** 15^2

  h 50^2 **i** 40^2 **j** 13^2

4 The graph shows the areas of squares and
their side lengths.

5 cm
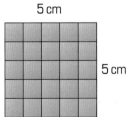
5 cm

3 cm
3 cm

$5 \times 5 = 25$

$3 \times 3 = 9$

Area (cm^2) / Side length (cm)

What are the side lengths of
squares with these areas?

  a $4 \ cm^2$ **b** $16 \ cm^2$ **c** $25 \ cm^2$

This spread will show you how to:

▶▶ Recognise squares of numbers to at least 12 × 12 and the corresponding roots.

KEYWORDS
Square root

The area of this square is 25 cm².

5 × 5 = 25, so
length of each side is 5 cm.

You say that the **square root** of 25 is 5.

Area = 25 cm²

▶ You write a square root like this:
square root of 25 = √25 = 5

The square root of 19 is not a whole number.
It must be more than 4 but less than 5, because √16 = 4 and √25 = 5.

16 cm²

√16 = 4

19 cm²

√19 = ?

25 cm²

√25 = 5

You can use the √ button on your calculator.
√19 is approximately 4.4.

example

Which 2 whole numbers do the square roots of these numbers lie between?
Use your calculator to find the square roots of these numbers to 1 decimal place.
a 92   b 126

....

a The square root of 92 must be more than 9 but less than 10,
because √81 = 9 and √100 = 10.

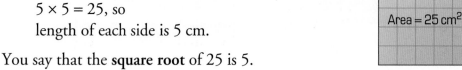 √ 9 2 = 9.5916630

√92 is approximately 9.6.

b The square root of 126 must be more than 11 but less than 12,
because √121 = 11 and √144 = 12.

√ 1 2 6 = 11.224972

√126 is approximately 11.2.

You can write √126 ≈ 11.2.
≈ means approximately equal to.

Exercise A3.6

1 Calculate the side length of each of these squares.
Do not measure them as they are not drawn to size.

a
Area =
49 cm²

b
Area =
36 cm²

c
Area =
64 cm²

2 Copy and complete these square root calculations.
a $\sqrt{81}$ **b** $\sqrt{1}$ **c** $\sqrt{100}$ **d** $\sqrt{4}$ **e** $\sqrt{64}$
f $\sqrt{36}$ **g** $\sqrt{16}$ **h** $\sqrt{25}$ **i** $\sqrt{9}$ **j** $\sqrt{49}$

3 a Draw the buttons that you would press to find
the value of $\sqrt{144}$ on your calculator.
b Use your calculator to find the value of $\sqrt{121}$.

4 Copy and complete these square root calculations.
You can use your calculator to help you.
a $\sqrt{144}$ **b** $\sqrt{169}$ **c** $\sqrt{196}$ **d** $\sqrt{225}$ **e** $\sqrt{256}$

5 Calculate the value of these.
a $4^2 + 4^2$ **b** $5^2 - 2^2$ **c** $7^2 + 1^2$ **d** $2^2 \times 2^2$

6 Find the missing squares to make these calculations work.
a $4^2 + \underline{}^2 = 20$ **b** $5^2 - \underline{}^2 = 24$ **c** $6^2 - \underline{}^2 = 27$
d $1^2 + \underline{}^2 = 2$ **e** $2^2 \times \underline{}^2 = 36$ **f** $10^2 \div \underline{}^2 = 25$

7
> You can approximate the value of the squares of decimals without a calculator.
> 4.7^2 is close to 5^2 so $4.7^2 \approx 25$ ($\approx$ means approximately equal to).

Copy and complete these approximations.
a $2.6^2 \approx \underline{}^2 = \underline{}$ **b** $5.9^2 \approx \underline{}^2 = \underline{}$ **c** $4.1^2 \approx \underline{}^2 = \underline{}$
d $9.7^2 \approx \underline{} = \underline{}$ **e** $3.4^2 \approx \underline{} = \underline{}$ **f** $7.8 \approx \underline{}$

8 Which of these statements are true?
a $\sqrt{16} = 4$ **b** $\sqrt{25} = 6$ **c** $\sqrt{81} = 8$ **d** $\sqrt{100} = 10$

9 ▸ Which 2 whole numbers do these square roots lie between?
▸ Use your calculator to find the square roots of these numbers to 1 decimal place.
The first one is started for you.
a $\sqrt{39}$ $\sqrt{39}$ is more than ⬚6 but less than ⬚7 .

$\sqrt{39} = $

b $\sqrt{62}$ **c** $\sqrt{78}$ **d** $\sqrt{112}$

You should know how to ...

1 Simplify expressions by collecting like terms.

Check out

1 Copy and complete these letter pyramids.

a
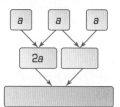

b
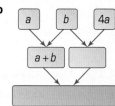

c
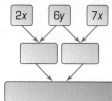

d
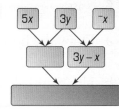

2 Develop from explaining a generalised relationship in words to expressing it in a formula using letters as symbols.

2 a Write an expression to say how many coins there are in each picture.
Use the symbol *n* for the unknown number of coins in the money box.

i

ii

b There were *m* coins in each money box, but some coins have been taken out.
How many coins are left in the money box?

i

ii

3 Use the relationship between the 4 operations.

3 Use inverse operations to calculate the input numbers in each question.
The first one has been started for you.

a
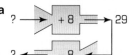

b
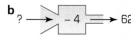

c

d

Geometrical reasoning

This unit will show you how to:

- ▶▶ Describe and visualise properties of flat shapes.
- ▶▶ Recognise parallel and perpendicular lines.
- ▶▶ Recognise and estimate angles.
- ▶▶ Calculate angles on a line and around a point.
- ▶▶ Use a protractor to measure angles.
- ▶▶ Classify triangles and quadrilaterals.
- ▶▶ Calculate angles in a triangle.

- ▶▶ Identify and use angle properties of triangles and quadrilaterals.
- ▶▶ Make shapes with increasing accuracy.
- ▶▶ Use a protractor to draw acute and obtuse angles.
- ▶▶ Describe and visualise properties of solid shapes.

There are triangles and circles all around you.

Before you start

You should know how to …

1 Identify and order acute, obtuse and right angles.

2 Recognise properties of rectangles.

Check in

1 **a** Write if each of these angles are acute, obtuse or right angle.

b Put the angles in order of size, starting with the smallest.

2 This shape is a rectangle.
   a How big are each of its angles?
   b What length is side CD?
   c What length is side BC?

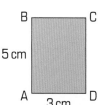

This spread will show you how to:
- ▶▶ Describe and visualise properties of flat shapes.
- ▶▶ Recognise parallel and perpendicular lines.

KEYWORDS

Parallel   Regular

Intersect   Congruent

Vertically opposite

Perpendicular

Parallel lines are always the same distance apart.

Perpendicular lines intersect at 90° – a right angle.

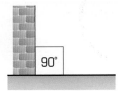

All other lines intersect at an angle that is not 90°.

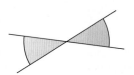

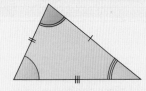

Train tracks are parallel.

A wall is perpendicular to the ground.

Vertically opposite angles are equal.

▶ Intersect means cross.

▶ Congruent shapes are exactly the same shape and size.

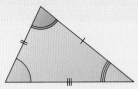

The shapes fit exactly on top of each other.

▶ Regular shapes have equal sides and equal angles.

This 4-sided shape is a square.

It is a regular quadrilateral, as each side is the same length, and each angle is the same size.

▶ This shows that sides are the same length:

▶ This shows that angles are the same size:

▶ This shows perpendicular lines:

▶ This shows parallel lines:

Exercise S1.1

1
  a Which line is parallel to TU?
  b Which line is parallel to JK?
  c Which line is perpendicular to JK?
  d Which line is perpendicular to TU?
  e Which angle is vertically opposite to angle *b*?

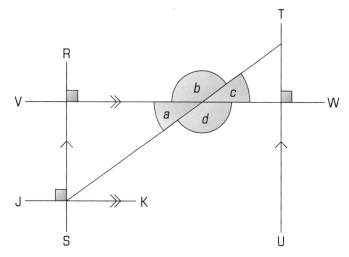

2 Match each shape to its congruent outline.

  a
  b
  i
  ii

  c
  d
  iii
  iv

  e
  v

3 Which of these shapes are regular?
If a shape is regular, write its number of
equal lines and equal angles.

  a
  b
  c
  d

  e
  f
  g
  h

This spread will show you how to:

▶▶ Recognise and estimate angles.
▶▶ Calculate angles on a line and around a point.
▶▶ Use a protractor to measure angles.

KEYWORDS

Acute   Obtuse
Full turn   Right angle
Degree (°)   Reflex

▶ **You measure an angle using degrees.**

Acute angle	Right angle	Obtuse angle	Reflex angle
Less than 90°	Exactly 90°	More than 90° Less than 180°	More than 180°

You can also estimate the size of an angle first.

---

example

For each of these angles:
a Estimate its size in degrees.
b Describe it.
c Measure its actual size.

i   **ii**   **iii**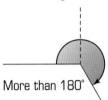

....

i Estimate: more than 90°
                  ~100°
This is an obtuse angle.
Measured value (using a
protractor) = 105°.

ii Estimate: less than 90°
                  ~50°
This is an acute angle.
Measured value = 52°

iii Estimate: more than 180°
                   less than 270°
                   ~240°
This is a reflex angle.
Measured value = 240°

You should know these angle properties:

There are 360° in 1 full turn.	There are 180° on a straight line.	Vertically opposite angles are equal.
		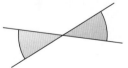

Exercise S1.2

1 ▶ Describe these angles.
  ▶ Estimate the size of these angles in degrees.

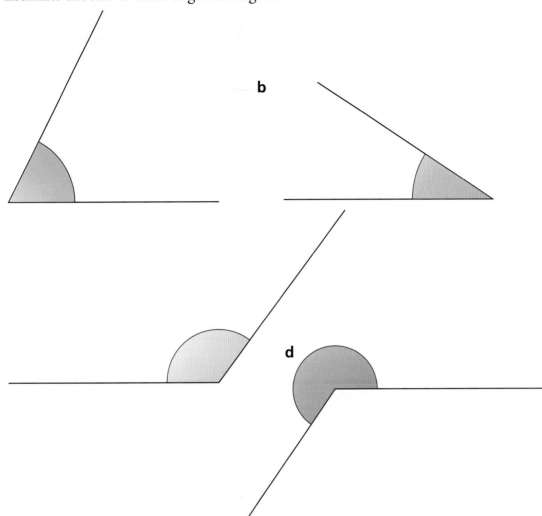

a

b

c

d

2 Measure accurately each of the angles in question 1.

3 Find the unknown angles in each diagram.
Do not measure them. They are not drawn to size.

a

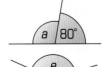

a 80°

b

50° b

c

c
200°

d

d
20°

e

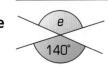

e
140°

f

f
140°

g

80°
g   g

h

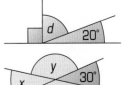

y
x   30°
z

This spread will show you how to:

▶▶ Classify triangles.
▶▶ Calculate angles in a triangle.

KEYWORDS
Right-angled Equal
Equilateral Scalene
Interior Exterior
Isosceles

You should know the properties of these triangles:

Right-angled

One 90° angle
marked ⌐

Equilateral

3 equal angles
3 equal sides

Isosceles

2 equal angles
2 equal sides

Scalene

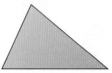

No equal angles
No equal sides

▶ The 3 angles in a triangle add up to 180°.

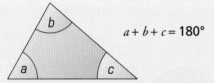

$a + b + c = 180°$

▶ An angle inside a shape is called an interior angle.

▶ An angle outside a shape made by extending a side is called an exterior angle.

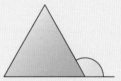

example

a Use your knowledge of angles to find the unknown angles in this diagram.
b What sort of triangle is it?

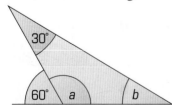

a The angles on a straight line add up to 180°. $a + 60° = 180°$
$$a = 180° - 60° = 120°$$
The angles in a triangle add up to 180°.
$$a + b + 30° = 180°$$
$$b = 180° - 120° - 30°$$
$$b = 30°$$

b The triangle has 2 equal angles so it is an isosceles triangle.

Exercise S1.3

1 Rachel has 5 strips of card.
Which 3 strips of card could she use to make:
  a a scalene triangle
  b an isosceles triangle
  c an equilateral triangle?

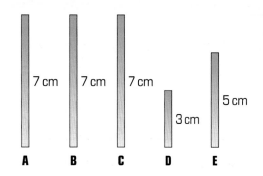

A   B   C   D   E

7 cm   7 cm   7 cm   3 cm   5 cm

2 Describe these triangles using the names: right-angled, equilateral, isosceles and scalene. Some of the triangles have 2 names.

a
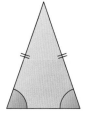

b
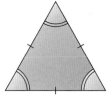

c

d
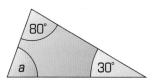

e
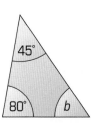

f
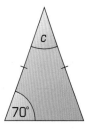

3 Use your knowledge of angles and triangles to find the unknown angles in these diagrams.

a

80°   a   30°

b

45°   80°   b

c
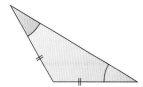
c   70°

d
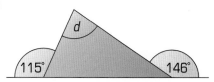
d   115°   146°

e
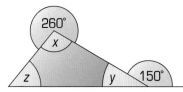
260°   x   z   y   150°

f

w

Quadrilaterals

This spread will show you how to:

▶▶ Classify quadrilaterals.

KEYWORDS
Quadrilateral   Side
Parallel   Polygon

A quadrilateral is a 4-sided shape.
▶ It has 4 straight sides and 4 angles.

You should know these special quadrilaterals and their properties.

Square

4 equal angles
4 equal sides
2 sets of parallel sides

Rhombus

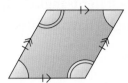

2 pairs of equal angles
4 equal sides
2 sets of parallel sides

Parallelogram

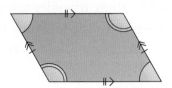

2 pairs of equal angles
2 sets of equal sides
2 sets of parallel sides

Rectangle

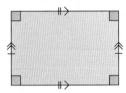

4 equal angles
2 sets of equal sides
2 sets of parallel sides

Trapezium

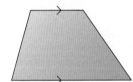

Usually has:
No equal angles
No equal sides
Always has:
1 set of parallel sides

Isosceles trapezium

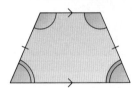

2 sets of equal angles
1 set of equal sides
1 set of parallel sides

Kite

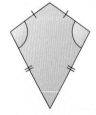

1 pair of equal angles
2 sets of equal sides
No parallel sides

Delta (arrowhead)

1 pair of equal angles
2 sets of equal sides
No parallel sides
1 reflex angle

Exercise S1.4

1 Rory is waiting for the lift at the Grand Hotel.
He notices that the design of the lift is made from
quadrilaterals.

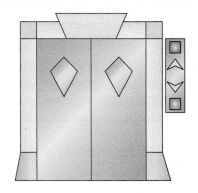

   a How many kites are there?
   b How many rectangles are there?
   c How many trapeziums are there?
   d How many squares are there?
   e How many deltas are there?

2 Copy these quadrilaterals. On each drawing mark:
   a Sides that are parallel:

   b Sides that are the same length:

   c Angles that are the same size: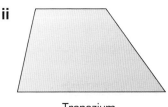

      Rectangle

ii

      Trapezium

iii

   Kite

3 **a** Describe the properties of this shape in
    your own words.
   b Name the shape.

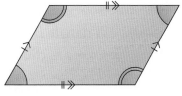

4 **a** Describe the properties of this shape in
    your own words.
   b Name the shape.

5 The angles in a regular polygon are all the same.
The sides of a regular polygon are all the same.
Only 1 quadrilateral is a regular polygon – which is it?

6 A quadrilateral has 4 equal angles. What shapes can it be?
Draw the shapes.

7 A quadrilateral has 4 equal sides. What shapes can it be?
Draw the shapes.

This spread will show you how to:

▶▶ Calculate angles in a triangle.
▶▶ Identify and use angle properties of triangles and quadrilaterals.

KEYWORDS
Triangle
Quadrilateral

A quadrilateral can be divided into 2 triangles using 1 line.

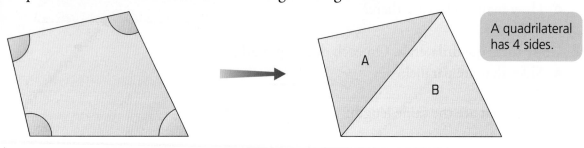

A quadrilateral has 4 sides.

You can find the sum of the 4 angles of the quadrilateral.

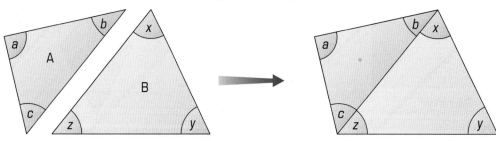

Triangle A
$a + b + c = 180°$

Triangle B
$x + y + z = 180°$

The angles in a quadrilateral =
angles in triangle A + angles in triangle B
$= 180° + 180° = 360°$.

▶ The sum of the angles in a quadrilateral is 360°.

Find the unknown angle in this quadrilateral.

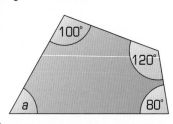

$a + 100° + 120° + 80° = 360°$
$a + 300° = 360°$
$a = 60°$

example

Exercise S1.5

1 Choose the 4 angles that together could make the 4 corners of a quadrilateral.

> The angles in a quadrilateral add up to 360°.

a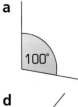
100°

b
90°

c
70°

d
55°

e
30°

f
140°

2 Find the unknown angles in these quadrilaterals.

a
100°
a   80°
100°

b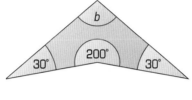
b
200°
30°   30°

c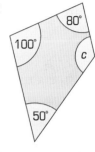
80°
100°
c
50°

d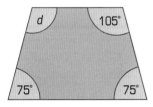
d   105°
75°   75°

e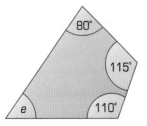
80°
115°
e   110°

f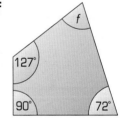
f
127°
90°   72°

3 Use your knowledge of quadrilaterals to find the unknown angles and sides in these shapes.

a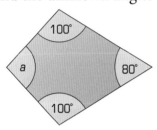
a   *b*
50°   130°

b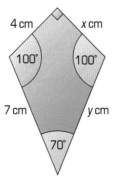
4 cm   *x* cm
100°   100°
7 cm   *y* cm
70°

c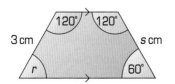
120° 120°
3 cm   *s* cm
r   60°

This spread will show you how to:
▶▶ Make shapes with increasing accuracy.

KEYWORDS
Ruler   Protractor
Midpoint
Perpendicular

When a line meets or crosses another line at 90° the lines are perpendicular.

Here are 2 ways that you can draw a pair of perpendicular lines.

1 Using a ruler and a set square.

Draw a line with your ruler.

Use a set square to draw the perpendicular.

Mark the right angle.

2 Using a ruler and a protractor.

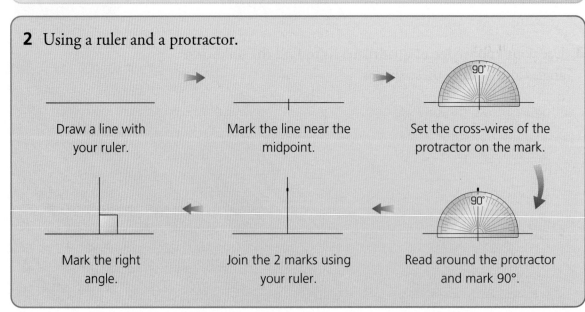

Draw a line with your ruler.

Mark the line near the midpoint.

Set the cross-wires of the protractor on the mark.

Mark the right angle.

Join the 2 marks using your ruler.

Read around the protractor and mark 90°.

Exercise S1.6

1 In each picture an angle is marked between a pair of lines.
Write whether each of the lines are perpendicular or not.

a

b

c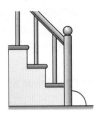

d

e

f

g

h

2 Use a set square or protractor to decide which 2 lines
are perpendicular to the red line.

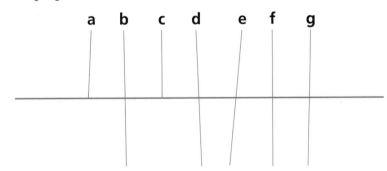

3 a Draw a horizontal line 8 cm long.
Label it RS.
Mark the midpoint of this line.
Draw a line perpendicular to RS.
Mark the right angle.

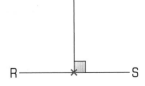

b Draw a vertical line 6 cm long.
Label it KL.
Mark the midpoint of this line.
Draw a line perpendicular to KL.
Mark the right angle.

This spread will show you how to:

▶▶ Use a protractor to draw acute and obtuse angles.
▶▶ Make shapes with increasing accuracy.

KEYWORDS
Protractor
Intersect

▶ You can use a protractor to draw angles.

60° is an acute angle.

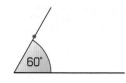

| Draw a line. | Measure 60° and mark angle. | Draw angle. |

130° is an obtuse angle.

| Draw a line. | Measure 130° and mark angle. | Draw angle. |

▶ You can construct a triangle using a ruler and a protractor.

example

Construct triangle ABC.

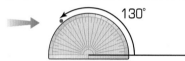

Side CB = 7 cm
∠C = 30°
∠B = 60°

| 7 cm | | |
| Draw side CB. | Measure ∠C (30°) and mark angle. | Draw angle. |

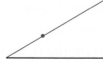

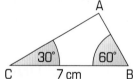

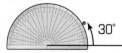

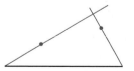

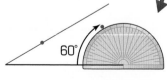

| Label triangle. | Draw angle so that it intersects line AC. | Measure ∠B (60°) and mark angle. |

Exercise S1.7

1 Read the scale on each protractor to measure each angle.
  i What is the size of each angle?
  ii Is it an acute or obtuse angle?

a

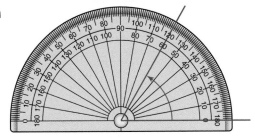

b

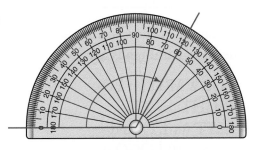

c

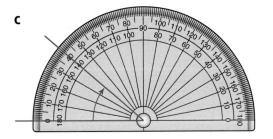

d

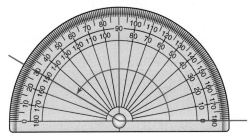

2 Use a ruler and a protractor to construct these acute angles.
  a 50°　　　**b** 35°　　　**c** 10°　　　**d** 83°

3 Use a ruler and a protractor to construct these obtuse angles.
  a 150°　　　**b** 125°　　　**c** 100°　　　**d** 174°

4 Use a ruler and a protractor to construct these triangles.

a

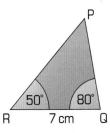

b

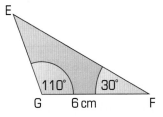

c

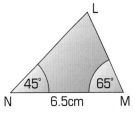

d

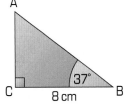

e

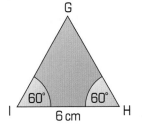

f

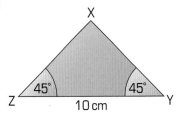

This spread will show you how to:

▶▶ Recognise angles.

KEYWORDS
LOGO

You can draw lines and angles using LOGO.
The basic commands are:

▶ FORWARD (or FD),
▶ RIGHT (or RT).
▶ LEFT (or LT), and
▶ 1 cm is 10 LOGO units.

You can draw this 'L' shape on 1 cm squared paper using these LOGO commands:

FD 20	Forward 20 units – 2 cm
LT 90	Turn left 90°
FD 30	Forward 30 units – 3 cm
RT 90	Turn right 90°
FD 50	Forward 50 units – 5 cm
LT 90	Turn left 90°
FD 20	Forward 20 units – 2 cm
LT 90	Turn left 90°
FD 70	Forward 70 units – 7 cm
LT 90	Turn left 90°
FD 50	Forward 50 units – 5 cm

The first move is always up the page.

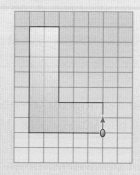

The start point is shown by a green 'turtle' or cursor on a computer screen. 🟢

example

Write the LOGO instructions for the construction of this shape.
Start your instructions from the cursor. 🟢

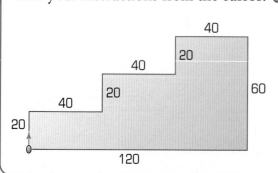

FD 20	FD 20
RT 90	RT 90
FD 40	FD 40
LT 90	RT 90
FD 20	FD 60
RT 90	RT 90
FD 40	FD 120
LT 90	

Exercise S1.8

1 Follow these instructions to draw a shape on squared paper.

Forward 10 squares
Turn right 90°
Forward 4 squares
Turn right 90°
Forward 10 squares
Turn right 90°
Forward 4 squares

> The first move is **up** the page.

2 Write the instructions to draw this shape.

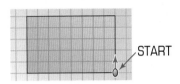

START

3 Follow these LOGO instructions to make a windmill shape.

Start at the green cursor –

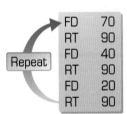

Repeat	FD	70
	RT	90
	FD	40
	RT	90
	FD	20
	RT	90

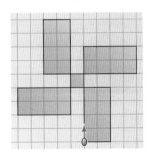

To continue, repeat the instructions.
The drawing shows you what the finished shape should look like.

4 Write the LOGO instructions for the construction of this shape.

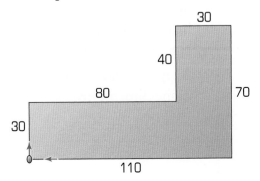

Start your instructions from the point marked by the cursor – .

This spread will show you how to:
▶▶ Describe and visualise properties of solid shapes.

KEYWORDS
3-D   Dimensions
Face   Edge
Apex   Base
Vertex (vertices)
Parallel

Solid shapes have 3 dimensions:
length, **w**idth and **h**eight.

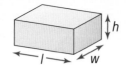

They are called 3-D shapes.

Here are some common 3-D shapes you need to know.

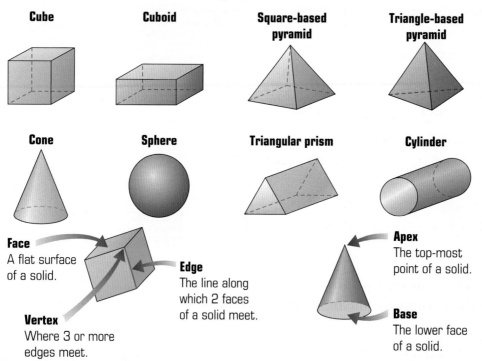

| Cube | Cuboid | Square-based pyramid | Triangle-based pyramid |
| Cone | Sphere | Triangular prism | Cylinder |

Face
A flat surface of a solid.

Edge
The line along which 2 faces of a solid meet.

Vertex
Where 3 or more edges meet.

Apex
The top-most point of a solid.

Base
The lower face of a solid.

---

example

This is a cuboid.

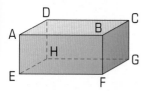

a Write the number of:
  i   edges
  ii faces
  iii vertices
b What shape are the faces?

a i   It has 12 edges.
  ii It has 6 faces.
  iii It has 8 vertices.
b The faces are all rectangles.
   Opposite faces all have the
   same dimensions.

Exercise S1.9

1 Look carefully at these shapes.

Cube   **Cone**   **Square-based pyramid**   **Sphere**   **Cylinder**

Which shape has:

a 2 circular faces and 2 edges?

b a square base and 4 triangular faces?

c 6 square faces?

d a circular base and an apex?

e no vertices or edges?

2 This is a cube.

a How many edges does it have?

b Name 1 edge which is parallel to edge CG.

c Name 1 edge which is perpendicular to edge AE.

d How many faces does it have?

f How many vertices does it have?

e What shape are the faces of a cube?

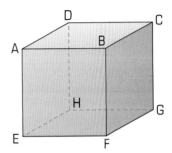

3 This is a triangular prism.

a How many edges does it have?

b Which edge is parallel to edge AB?

c How long is edge BC?

d How many faces does it have?

e Does it have any parallel faces?

f Does it have any perpendicular faces? If so, name them.

g What shape is face ABC? Describe it as fully as you can.

h What shape is face BCFE?

i How many vertices does it have?

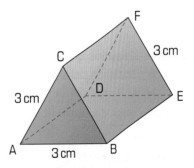

Parallel faces are always the same distance apart.
The angle between perpendicular faces is a right angle (90°).

You should know how to ...

1 Use a protractor to measure angles.

2 Classify quadrilaterals.

Check out

1 Use a protractor to measure these angles.

a

b

c

d

2 **a** ▶ Copy this quadrilateral.
    ▶ Mark the sides that are parallel.
    ▶ Mark the sides that are the same length.
    ▶ Mark the angles that are the same size.

Rhombus

  b ▶ Describe the geometrical properties of this shape.
    ▶ Name the shape.

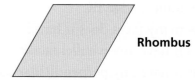
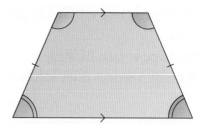
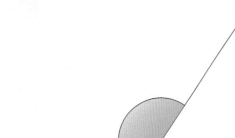

1 Handling data

This unit will show you how to:

▶▶ Solve a problem by representing, extracting and interpreting data.

▶▶ Explain methods and reasoning.

▶▶ Find the mode, median and mean of a set of data.

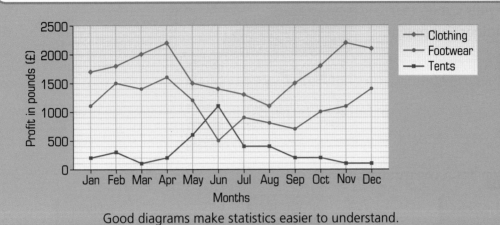

Good diagrams make statistics easier to understand.

Before you start

You should know how to ...

1 Read data in a frequency table.

2 Read simple bar charts.

Check in

1 The frequency table shows how many portions of fruit and vegetables Sam and Catherine ate in 1 week.

Day	Mon	Tue	Wed	Thur	Fri
Sam	4	2	3	2	2
Catherine	4	3	4	4	3

a How many portions does Sam eat on Friday?

b On how many days does Sam eat 5 portions?

c On how many days does Catherine eat 5 portions?

d Who eats more fruit and vegetables overall?

2 The bar chart shows eye colour of students.

a What is the most common eye colour?

b How many students have green eyes?

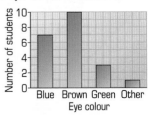

This spread will show you how to:
- ▶▶ Solve a problem by representing, extracting and interpreting data.
- ▶▶ Explain methods and reasoning.

KEYWORDS

Data — Interpret
Bar chart — Source
Questionnaire

Jimmy runs a shop that sells outdoor equipment.

The Mountain Range Shop

OPEN

The shop has 3 departments.

Footwear

Tents

Outdoor clothing

The shop has been making less and less profit each month.
Jimmy needs to find out why this is happening.
To do this he uses the handling data cycle.

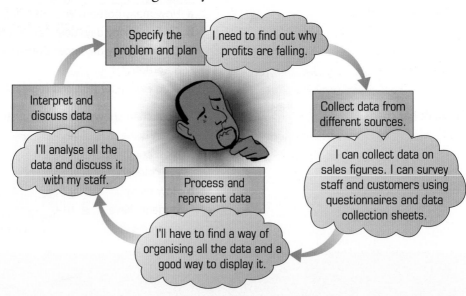

Specify the problem and plan — I need to find out why profits are falling.

Interpret and discuss data

I'll analyse all the data and discuss it with my staff.

Collect data from different sources.

I can collect data on sales figures. I can survey staff and customers using questionnaires and data collection sheets.

Process and represent data

I'll have to find a way of organising all the data and a good way to display it.

Exercise D1.1

1 Jimmy asks his workers for ideas to make more profit.
  a Pick 1 proposal that you think is a good idea. Explain why.
  b Pick 1 proposal that you think is a bad idea. Explain why.

2 Here are the parts of the handling data cycle.
Write them in the correct order and draw the handling data cycle.

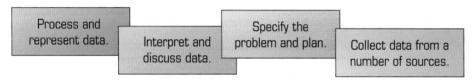

3 Here is a graph showing profit for the Mountain Range Shop over 12 months.

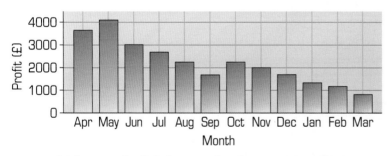

This is a bar chart. The height of each bar gives the total profit each month.

  a In which month did they make the most profit?
  b In which month did they make the least profit?
  c In which month did they make £3000 profit?
  d How much profit did they make in November?
  e Does the graph support Jimmy's statement that profit is falling?

This spread will show you how to:

▶▶ Solve a problem by representing, extracting and interpreting data.

KEYWORDS

Primary data
Secondary data

▶ Primary data is data you collect yourself.

The shop staff fill in a data collection sheet for each customer.

DATA COLLECTION SHEET

	UNDER 25	AGE 25 to 50	OVER 50	M or F	PURCHASE	SPEND
1.		✓		M	BOOTS	£45
2.			✓	M	SOCKS	£4
3.		✓		F	HAT + GLOVES	£12
4.	✓			M	TENT	£95
5.		✓		F	JACKET	£39
6.	✓			F	TRAINERS	£67
7.		✓		M	JUMPER	£26

Customers are asked to fill in a questionnaire about their visit to the shop.

CUSTOMER QUESTIONNAIRE

Please score each aspect of your shopping experience:
1 = POOR **5** = EXCELLENT

		1	2	3	4	5
1.	Value for money					✓
2.	Layout of shop		✓			✓
3.	Attitude of staff					
4.	Quality of products			✓		
5.	Speed of service			✓		

These are both good ways of collecting primary data.

▶ Secondary data is data that has already been collected.

The accountant produces sales figures for the past year.

	A	B	C	D	E
1	**Month**	**Income**	**Credits**	**Outgoings**	**% Discount**
2	1	10 937	195	2971	27%
3	2	11 215	672	3025	30%
4	3	15 916	1195	3193	25%

Exercise D1.2

1 Jimmy looks at the data collection sheets filled in on the first day.
He does a tally of customers by gender.

Gender	Tally	Frequency
Male	ЖHT ЖHT ЖHT ЖHT ЖHT ЖHT ЖHT III	?
Female	ЖHT ЖHT ЖHT ЖHT ЖHT II	?

These are frequency tables.

a How many males visited the shop?
b How many females visited the shop?

2 He then does a tally of customers by age.

Age group	Tally	Frequency
Under 25	ЖHT ЖHT ЖHT ЖHT I	?
25 to 50	ЖHT ЖHT ЖHT ЖHT ЖHT ЖHT II	?
Over 50	ЖHT ЖHT II	?

a How many under 25s visited the shop?
b Which age group had the smallest number of customers?
c Which age group had the largest number of customers?

3 Annie collects data from 5 customers. Jimmy wants data from
at least 100 customers.
Why do you think he needs so many?

4 Jimmy totals the results from the questionnaires.

	Poor				Excellent
	1	2	3	4	5
1. Value for money	3	6	8	14	9
2. Layout of shop	12	14	12	2	0

a Do most customers think that they are getting good value for money?
b Do most customers think that the shop is well laid out?

5 Here are the sales for each department in June and October.

Department sales for June		
Footwear	Tents	Clothes
£2520	£1302	£725
Department sales for October		
Footwear	Tents	Clothes
£1565	£240	£2180

a Which department has the worst sales in June?
b Which department has the best sales in October?

This spread will show you how to:

▶▶ Find the mode, median and mean of a set of data.

KEYWORDS
Mean   Mode
Median   Average
Range

The mean, median and mode are averages.

▶ The mean is the total of the values divided by the number of values.
▶ The median is the middle number when the data are in order.
▶ The mode is the most common value.

example

11 customers are asked how many credit cards they have.
The numbers of cards are recorded in order, smallest to largest:
        1, 2, 2, 2, 2, 3, 3, 4, 4, 5, 5
Find: **a** the mean,   **b** the median,   **c** the mode.

a The total number of cards is 33.
   There are 11 values.
   $33 \div 11 = 3$
   The mean is 3.
b Find the middle number.
   1, 2, 2, 2, 2, **3**, 3, 4, 4, 5, 5
   The median is 3.
c There are more 2s in the data
   than any other number.
   The mode is 2.

To find the median when there are an even number of
values, find the midpoint between the 2 middle numbers.

example

What is the median of 6, 8, 9 and 12?

The midpoint is between 8 and 9.   6, 8, 9, 12
Halfway between 8 and 9 is 8.5.   ↑
The median is 8.5.

▶ The range tells you how spread out the values are.
   Range = greatest value – least value

Exercise D1.3

1 Here are the colours of shirts sold in 1 week.

blue	red	blue	green	green	blue	yellow	red	blue	red
yellow	blue	red	green	blue	green	red	blue	green	blue

a Copy and complete this frequency table for the shirts.

b What is the modal colour of shirts sold?

Colour	Tally	Frequency
Blue		

2 Customers were asked how many times they had visited the shop during the past year. Here are their replies.

You can have more than one mode.

2	1	3	1	5	3	2	0	1	4	3	0
1	5	4	3	3	1	3	0	6	1	0	2

a Draw a frequency table like the one in question 1 for the results.

b What is the modal number of visits the customers made?

3 Here is a group of customers lining up to pay.

a Write their heights out in order – smallest to biggest.

b What is the median height of the group?

177 cm   198 cm   174 cm   165 cm   188 cm

4 8 customers enter the shop. Their ages in years are:

22, 55, 18, 32, 42, 37, 20 and 28

a Write the ages out in order – smallest to biggest.

b What is the median age of this group?

5 During the week a number of customers pay by cheque. Here is a record of the numbers of cheques paid in each day.

Mon	Tue	Wed	Thur	Fri	Sat
5	10	8	12	9	20

The mean is not always a whole number.

What is the mean number of cheques paid in each day?

6 What is the mean of this group of values?

6   4   4   5   8   3   5   2   3   5

This spread will show you how to:

▶▶ Solve a problem by representing, extracting and interpreting data in charts and diagrams.

KEYWORDS
Pie chart
Bar chart
Comparative bar chart
Line graph

Jimmy uses charts and graphs to display his findings.

He uses a **bar chart** to compare how much profit each department makes in 1 month.

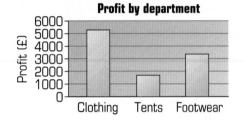

Profit by department

▶ A bar chart is useful for comparing one category with another.

He uses a **comparative bar chart** to show the age groups of customers visiting each department in 1 day.

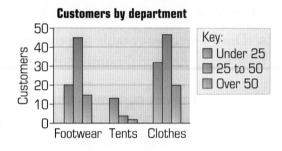

Customers by department

Key:
■ Under 25
■ 25 to 50
■ Over 50

▶ A comparative bar chart is useful for comparing within categories.

He uses a **line graph** to show how many people are in the shop in 1 day.

Customers in shop in a day

▶ A line graph is useful for showing how things change over time.

He uses a **pie chart** to compare the number of female customers with the total number of customers.

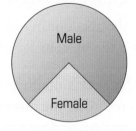

Customers by gender during July

Male

Female

▶ A pie chart is useful for comparing each category within the total.

Exercise D1.4

1 The Mountain Range Shop sells 4 makes of jackets. The frequency table shows jackets sold in 1 month.

Make of jacket	Tally	Frequency
Kold King	ЖИ III	8
Alto	III	3
X-treme	ЖИ ЖИ I	11
Degrees North	ЖИ I	6

Copy and complete the bar chart using the data from the frequency table.

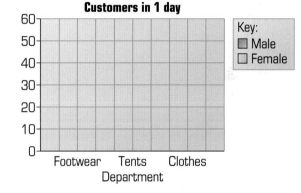

Sales of jackets

2 The table shows the number of male and female customers visiting each department in 1 day. Copy and complete the comparative bar chart.

	Department		
	Footwear	Tents	Clothes
Male	50	10	45
Female	25	5	55

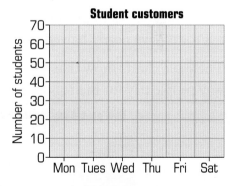

Customers in 1 day

Key:
- ■ Male
- □ Female

3 The table shows how many students visit the shop in each day of 1 week.

Day	Mon	Tue	Wed	Thu	Fri	Sat
Number of students	30	15	35	30	45	65

Use the data from the table to copy and complete this line graph.

Student customers

4 This pie chart shows the ages of customers visiting the shop on 1 day.

a Copy and complete this table to show the fraction of customers in each age group.

Age group	Under 25	25 to 50	Over 50
Fraction	$\frac{1}{4}$		

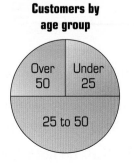

Customers by age group

b There were 200 customers in the shop that day. How many customers were under 25?

This spread will show you how to:

▶▶ Solve a problem by extracting and interpreting data.

KEYWORDS
Line graph   Pie chart
Trend

This table shows how much profit the Mountain Range Shop
made in the previous 6 years.

Year	1	2	3	4	5	6
Profit	£13 500	£12 200	£9800	£9000	£8200	£7300

You can display this data on a line graph.

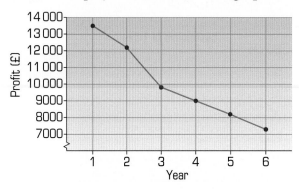

The 'zig-zag' shows that the values
on the vertical scale start above zero.

From this data you can see that:

▶ The trend is profits are falling.
▶ The biggest fall in profits was between years 2 and 3.
▶ Profits have nearly halved over 6 years.

To see a **trend**, look to see if the
values are generally increasing or
decreasing on the graph.

These pie charts show that there has been a change in the
way people pay for their shopping over the past 5 years.

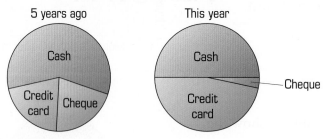

How people pay for their shopping

From this data you can see that:

▶ More people are using credit cards to pay for their shopping.
▶ Very few people now pay by cheque.

The pie charts do not tell you whether people are spending
more or less money in the shop.

Exercise D1.5

1 This table shows the number of customers that visit the shop over 12 months.

Month	Jan	Feb	Mar	Apr	May	Jun	Jul	Aug	Sep	Oct	Nov	Dec
Number of customers	1125	1302	1870	2482	2141	1840	1665	1103	1890	1910	2032	2395

a Which are the busiest 3 months?

b Which are the quietest 3 months?

c Why might business be good around December?

d Why might business be bad around August?

2 The line graph shows the profits made by the 3 departments (Footwear, Tents and Clothing) in 1 year.

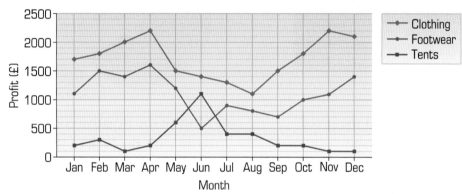

a In which month does:

   i tents,   **ii** footwear,   **iii** clothing

   make its biggest profit?

b How much profit did Footwear make in February?

c Why do you think Tents sell better in Spring than in Winter?

d Which department is making the smallest profit?

3 Jimmy records the bad points that customers have mentioned.
He shows this information on 2 pie charts, 1 for women and 1 for men.

a What is the biggest bad point for men?

b What is the biggest bad point for women?

c Which bad point did men and women mention equally?

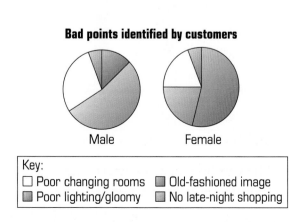

Bad points identified by customers

Male   Female

Key:
☐ Poor changing rooms   ▨ Old-fashioned image
▧ Poor lighting/gloomy   ▨ No late-night shopping

This spread will show you how to:

▶▶ Solve a problem by representing, extracting and interpreting data.

▶▶ Explain methods and reasoning.

KEYWORDS
Data

To complete the handling data cycle, Jimmy meets with the staff to discuss the data and use it to make changes.

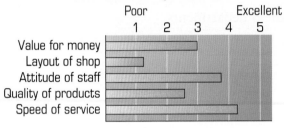

Mean scores from questionnaire

Customer concerns

Jimmy's customers think:

▶ The attitude of the staff and the speed of service is better than average.

▶ Value for money and quality of product is about average.

▶ The layout of the shop is poor.

▶ Most of the negative concerns are to do with the look of the shop.

▶ A few people wanted to be able to shop in the evenings.

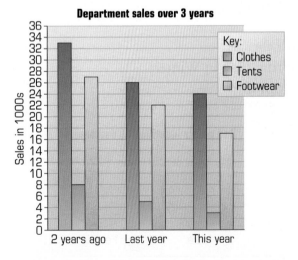

Department sales over 3 years

Spending on decorating over 5 years

4 years ago	3 years ago	2 years ago	1 year ago	This year
£2685	£1360	£480	£185	£64

▶ The amount of money spent on decorating over the last 5 years has gone down each year.

This data might explain why most of the customer concerns were to do with the look of the shop.

▶ The Clothes department has the biggest sales and the Tents department has the smallest sales.

▶ Sales have gone down over the last 3 years in all departments.

Exercise D1.6

1 Here are the sales figures for each department for the year after the changes and the year before. What do the graphs show?

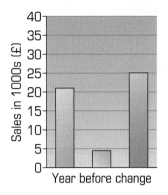

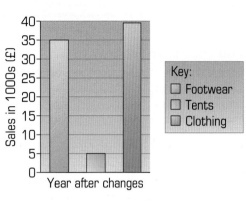

Key:
☐ Footwear
☐ Tents
☐ Clothing

2 Jimmy did a survey of customers to find out more about late-night shopping.
He asked customers if they would shop in the evening and, if so, which day would they shop on.

Interested in late-night shopping?	No	Yes
Frequency	45	55

a Draw graphs to show this data, from these tables.

Day	Mon	Tue	Wed	Thur	Fri	Sat
Frequency	4	13	3	15	10	10

b What do your graphs show?

3 Here are the ideas put forward after Jimmy discussed his findings with his staff.

1. Open late on Tuesday and Thursday evenings.
2. Paint the shop.
3. Change the name of the shop – what could the new name be?
4. Improve the lighting.
5. Repair the changing rooms.
6. Close down 1 department for 8 months each year and use the space to sell the things that customers want – which department would you close?
7. Cut prices in all departments.
8. Replace all of the staff.
9. Have a Spring Sale in January and a Summer Sale in August.
10. Advertise the Tents department more positively.

Use the charts, graphs and tables in this unit to help you.
a Choose 3 of the changes that would improve business for the shop.
b Explain each choice and explain which piece of data you used to make your decision.

You should know how to ...

1 Solve a problem by representing, extracting and interpreting data.

Check out

1 The table shows the number of ice creams sold by a shop in 1 week.

Day	Mon	Tue	Wed	Thur	Fri	Sat	Sun
Ice creams sold	8	2	3	13	10	20	25

a Draw a bar chart to show this data.

b On which day did the shop sell the most ice creams?

c On which day did the shop sell the fewest ice creams?

The line graph shows the temperature in the same week.

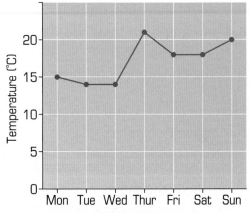

d Which day was the warmest?

e Which days were the coldest?

f What does the data tell you about ice cream sales in the week?

2 Find the mode, median and mean of a set of data.

2 Find:

a the mode

b the median

c the mean

of this data:

3, 4, 4, 5, 6, 6, 6, 7, 8, 8

Perimeter, area and volume

This unit will show you how to:

- Read and plot coordinates in all quadrants.
- Know and use the formula for the area of a rectangle.
- Find the area of a triangle.
- Use, read and write standard metric units.
- Calculate the perimeter and area of simple compound shapes.
- Find volume by counting cubes.
- Find the surface area of cubes and cuboids.
- Visualise 3-D shapes from 2-D drawings.
- Know imperial units.
- Know rough equivalents.
- Suggest suitable units to measure length, mass and capacity.

Some people just go round the perimeter of the ice rink.
Others cover the whole area.

Before you start

You should know how to ...

1 Read and plot coordinates in the first quadrant.

2 Find the area of a rectangle.

Check in

1 a What are the coordinates of each of the points A, B and C?

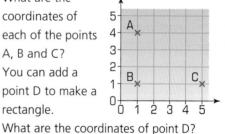

b You can add a point D to make a rectangle.
What are the coordinates of point D?

2 What is the area of each of these rectangles?

a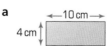

b

Coordinates

This spread will show you how to:
▶▶ Read and plot coordinates in all quadrants.

KEYWORDS
Quadrant   Coordinate
Origin   Perpendicular
Axes

▶ A grid has 2 axes: the x-axis and the y-axis.
They are perpendicular to each other.

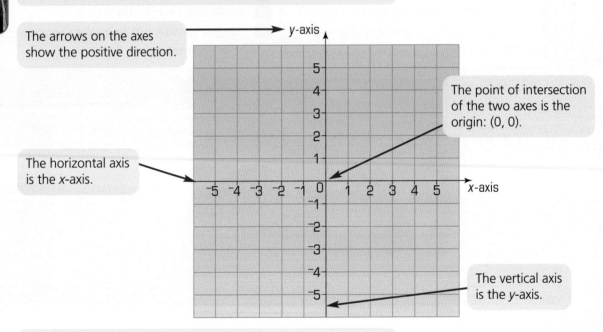

The arrows on the axes show the positive direction.

The horizontal axis is the x-axis.

The point of intersection of the two axes is the origin: (0, 0).

The vertical axis is the y-axis.

▶ You count across first, then up.

example

a What letter will you find at coordinates ($^-4$, 3) on this grid?

b Give the coordinates of M.

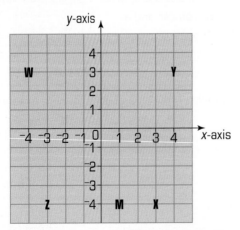

a Start at the origin. Go 4 left on the x-axis.
You get to $^-4$.
Then go 3 up the y-axis and you find W.

b To find M, go right 1 along the x-axis.
Then go 4 down the y-axis.
You get to $^-4$.
M is at coordinates (1, $^-4$).

Exercise S2.1

1 What letter will you find at each of these coordinates?

  a (4, 2)
  b (4, ⁻2)
  c (⁻2, ⁻2)
  d (5, 4)
  e (1, ⁻5)
  f (⁻2, 5)
  g (⁻6, ⁻5)
  h (⁻5, 2)

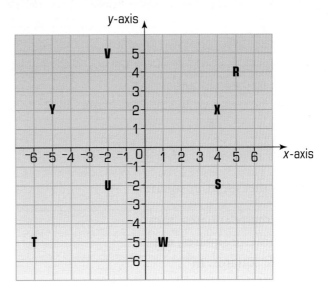

2 Write the coordinates for these letters.

  A
  B
  C
  D
  E
  F
  G
  H

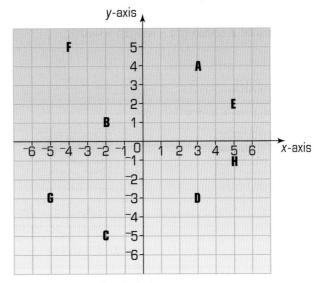

3 a Copy the axes and plot these coordinates.

  (2, 4) (⁻2, ⁻2) (⁻6, ⁻4) (⁻2, 2)

  b Join the coordinates to make a shape.
  Name the shape.

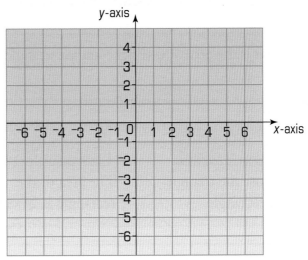

S2.2 Area of a triangle

This spread will show you how to:

▶▶ Know and use the formula for the area of a rectangle.
▶▶ Find the area of a triangle.
▶▶ Use, read and write standard metric units.

KEYWORDS
Area   Triangle
Length   Width

▶ **The area of a shape is the amount of space it covers.**

Area is measured in squares:

▶ millimetre squares, mm^2
▶ centimetre squares, cm^2
▶ metre squares, m^2
▶ kilometre squares, km^2.

▶ **Area of a rectangle = length × width**

To find the area of this rectangle, multiply the length by the width.

$$l \times w = 4 \times 3 = 12 \ cm^2$$

The area of this rectangle is $12 \ cm^2$.

The diagonal line divides the rectangle into 2 halves.

The shaded part is a right-angled triangle. The area of the triangle is $6 \ cm^2$.

▶ **The area of a triangle is half of the area of the rectangle that encloses it.**

example

What is the area of this right-angled triangle?

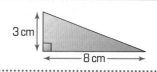

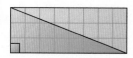

Enclose the triangle in a rectangle.

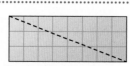

The area of the rectangle is $24 \ cm^2$.

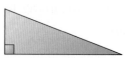

The area of the triangle is half the area of the rectangle = $12 \ cm^2$.

Exercise S2.2

1 Draw each rectangle and find its area and perimeter.

a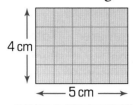

4 cm

←— 5 cm —→

> The perimeter of a shape is the distance round the edge.

b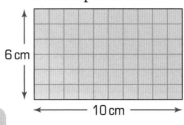

6 cm

←——— 10 cm ———→

c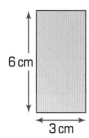

6 cm

3 cm

2 Find the area of each right-angled triangle.
▶ Divide the area of the rectangle that encloses it by 2.

a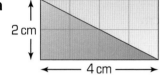

2 cm

←— 4 cm —→

b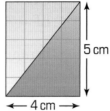

5 cm

←— 4 cm —→

c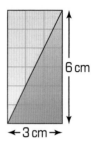

6 cm

←3 cm→

d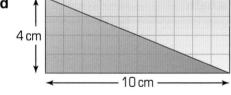

4 cm

←——— 10 cm ———→

e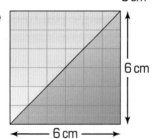

6 cm

←——— 6 cm ———→

f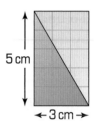

5 cm

←3 cm→

3 Sketch each right-angled triangle and find its area.

a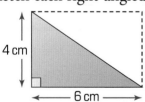

4 cm

←— 6 cm —→

b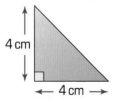

4 cm

←— 4 cm —→

c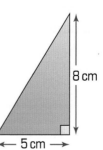

8 cm

←— 5 cm —→

d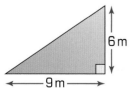

6 m

←— 9 m —→

e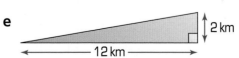

2 km

←——— 12 km ———→

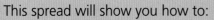

This spread will show you how to:

▶▶ Calculate the perimeter and area of compound shapes.
▶▶ Know and use the formula for the area of a rectangle.
▶▶ Use, read and write standard metric units.

KEYWORDS

Perimeter   Total
Area   Rectangle

▶ The perimeter of a shape is the distance round the edge.

example

Find the perimeter of this shape.

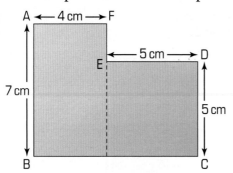

The missing lengths are BC and EF.
BC = AF + ED.
  = 4 + 5 = 9 cm
CD + EF = BA.
EF = 7 − 5 = 2 cm

Perimeter = 7 + 9 + 5 + 5 + 2 + 4 = 32 cm

To find the area of any rectangle you multiply the length by the width.

▶ **Area** = $l \times w$

Area is measured in squares.

You can split some compound shapes into different rectangles.

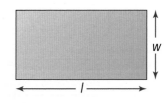

A compound shape is made up of smaller shapes.

example

Find the area of this L shape.

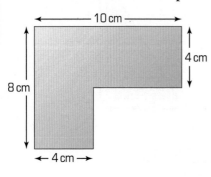

Area of rectangle A = $10 \times 4 = 40 \text{ cm}^2$
Area of rectangle B = $4 \times 4 = 16 \text{ cm}^2$
      Total area = $40 + 16 = 56 \text{ cm}^2$

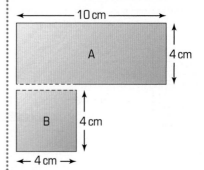

Exercise S2.3

1 ► Find the perimeter of each shape in cm.
► Find the area of each shape in cm^2.

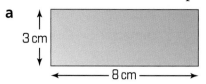

a 3 cm, 8 cm

b 5 cm, 5 cm

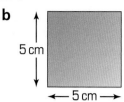

c 4 cm, 9 cm

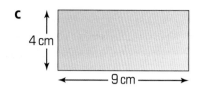

2 ► Find the area of each compound shape.
► Find the perimeter of each compound shape.
The shapes have been split up into rectangles to help you.

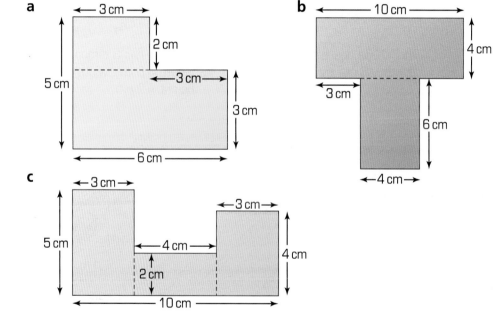

a 3 cm, 2 cm, 5 cm, 3 cm, 3 cm, 6 cm

b 10 cm, 4 cm, 3 cm, 6 cm, 4 cm

c 3 cm, 3 cm, 5 cm, 4 cm, 4 cm, 2 cm, 10 cm

3 ► Find the perimeter of each compound shape.
► Find the area of each compound shape.
Split the shapes up into rectangles to help you.

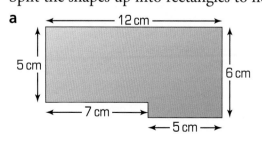

a 12 cm, 5 cm, 6 cm, 7 cm, 5 cm

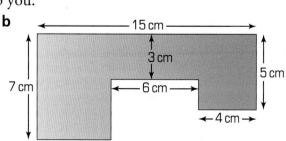

b 15 cm, 3 cm, 7 cm, 6 cm, 5 cm, 4 cm

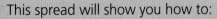

This spread will show you how to:

▶▶ Know and use the formula for the area of a rectangle.
▶▶ Find volume by counting cubes.

You can describe shapes by their dimensions.

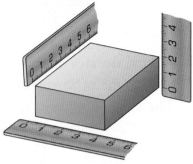

Distance has only 1
dimension (1-D).
This distance is 6 cm.

This shape has 2 dimensions (2-D):
length = 6 cm and width = 4 cm.

This box has 3 dimensions (3-D):
length = 6 cm, width = 4 cm and
height = 2 cm.

▶ The volume of a 3-D shape is the amount of space it takes up.

Volume is measured in cubes.

Small volumes are measured
in centimetre cubes: cm^3.

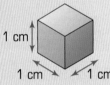

1 cm

1 cm   1 cm

Larger volumes are measured
in metre cubes: m^3.

1 m

1 m

1 m

These shapes are made using 1 centimetre cubes.

This shape is made from 8 cubes.
Its volume is 8 centimetre cubes,
written 8 cm^3.

This cuboid has a volume of 6 cm^3.

This shape is made from 12 cubes.
Its volume is 12 centimetre cubes,
written 12 cm^3.

Another layer is added ...
the volume of this cuboid is 12 cm^3.

Exercise S2.4

1 Write if each of these is 1-D, 2-D or 3-D.

a
b
c
d
e

f
g
h
i
j

2 These solid shapes are made from 1 cm cubes.
What is the volume of each shape?

a
b
c

d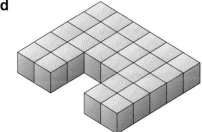
e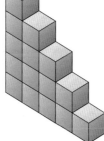
f

3 Max puts these 1 cm cubes together to make a cuboid.
   a What is the volume of the cuboid?   **b** Max adds another layer to the cuboid.
                                          What is the volume of the new cuboid?

4 These cuboids are made from 1 cm cubes.
What is the volume of each cuboid?

a
b
c

This spread will show you how to:

▶▶ Visualise 3-D shapes from 2-D drawings.
▶▶ Find the volume and surface area of cubes and cuboids.
▶▶ Calculate the area of shapes made from rectangles.

KEYWORDS

Net   Surface area
Cuboid   Volume

You can make boxes from flat shapes called nets.

This net ...   ... folds to make this cuboid.

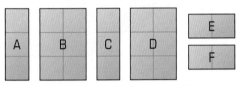

The net has 6 rectangular parts.   The cuboid has 6 faces.

A + B + C + D + E + F = 22 squares   6 cubes

The cuboid has a surface area of 22 cm^2 The cuboid has a volume of 6 cm^3

▶ The area of the net is the surface area of the cuboid.

example

Here is a net and the cuboid that it makes.

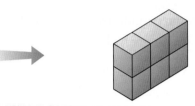

a What is the surface area of the cuboid?
b What is the volume of the cuboid?

....

a Here are the 6 parts of the net.

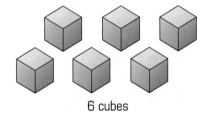

9 cm^2 9 cm^2

E 3 cm^2
F 3 cm^2

3 cm^2 3 cm^2

Add the areas of each part:
The surface area of the cuboid is 30 cm^2.

b The cuboid is made of 9 centimetre cubes.

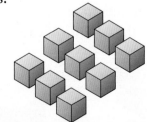

The volume of the cuboid is 9 cm^3.

Exercise S2.5

1 Here is a net and the cuboid that it makes.

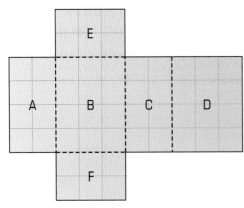 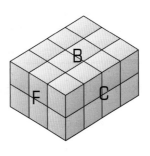

   a What is the opposite face to F?
   b What is the opposite face to C?
   c What is the opposite face to B?
   d What is the area of the net?
   e What is the surface area of the cuboid?
   f What is the volume of the cuboid?

2 Match each net to the cuboid it makes.

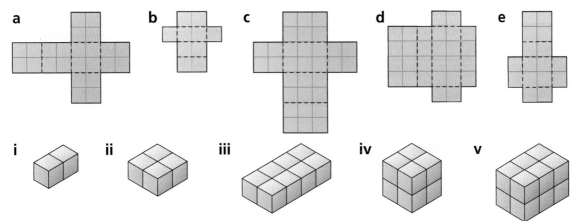

3 a What is the surface area of each cuboid?
   b What is the volume of each cuboid?

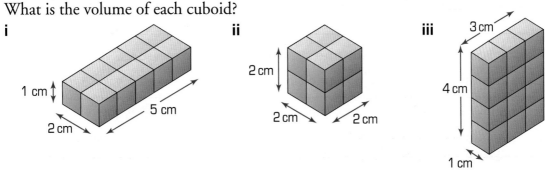

This spread will show you how to:

▶▶ Use, read and write standard metric units.
▶▶ Know imperial units and rough equivalents.
▶▶ Suggest suitable units.

KEYWORDS

Metric   Mass
Length   Capacity
Imperial Approximately (≈)

You need to know all of these measures:

▶ Length is a measure of distance.

Metric		
10 millimetres (mm)	=	1 centimetre
100 centimetres (cm)	=	1 metre
1000 metres (m)	=	1 kilometre (km)

Equivalents	
1 inch	≈ $2\frac{1}{2}$ centimetres
1 foot	≈ 30 centimetres
1 yard	≈ 1 metre
5 miles	≈ 8 kilometres

Imperial		
12 inches (")	=	1 foot
3 feet (')	=	1 yard
1760 yard (yds)	=	1 mile

▶ Mass is a measure of how heavy an object is.

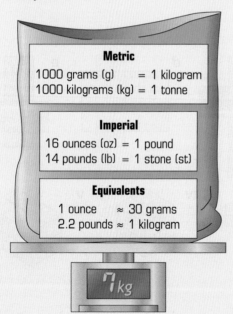

Metric
1000 grams (g)   = 1 kilogram
1000 kilograms (kg) = 1 tonne

Imperial
16 ounces (oz) = 1 pound
14 pounds (lb) = 1 stone (st)

Equivalents
1 ounce   ≈ 30 grams
2.2 pounds ≈ 1 kilogram

▶ Capacity is a measure of the amount of liquid a container will hold.

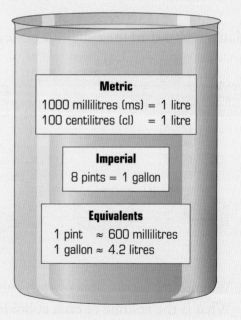

Metric
1000 millilitres (ms) = 1 litre
100 centilitres (cl)   = 1 litre

Imperial
8 pints = 1 gallon

Equivalents
1 pint   ≈ 600 millilitres
1 gallon ≈ 4.2 litres

example

Change these measurements into approximate metric measures.

'John picked up the 8 pound (lb) weight and threw it 21 yards (yds).'

8 pounds is *about* 4 kilograms and 21 yards is *about* 21 metres so:

'John picked up the 4 kilogram (kg) weight and threw it 21 metres (m).'

Exercise S2.6

1 Use the tables on page 96 to write which amount is greater.

   a 1 pint or 1 litre?   **b** 1 mile or 1 kilometre?

   c 1 pound or 1 kilogram?   **d** 1 ounce or 1 gram?

   e 1 inch or 1 centimetre?   **f** 1 foot or 1 metre?

2 Ricky goes to France. He has to change metric measures into imperial to understand. Write the approximate imperial equivalent to each of these.

a  This carton holds 3 litres of milk.

b St. Omer is 16 kilometres from here.

c  I think you would love 5 kilograms of this old, ripe cheese.

d 5 metres of blue ribbon

e 500 grams of my finest chocolate.

f The cake is 10 centimetres across.

3 Monsieur Le Grande from Paris is visiting the UK. He has to change imperial measures into metric to understand these signs.

Write the approximate metric equivalent to each sign.

a  Dover 15 miles

b  ONE PINT FARMER'S MILK **1 pint**

c  Stop 50 yards ahead

d 5 pounds of oranges for £2

e DEEP END! 6 FEET DEEP

4 Suggest an appropriate metric unit and imperial unit to measure:

   a the height of a tree

   b the mass of a mouse

   c the distance from London to Paris

   d the length of a bee's wing

   e the capacity of a milk carton

   f the mass of a bag of sugar.

You should know how to ...

1 Read and plot coordinates in all quadrants.

2 Calculate the perimeter and area of simple compound shapes.

Check out

1 a What are the coordinates of each of the points A, B and C?

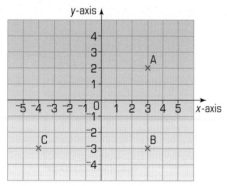

b Copy the axes and the points onto 1 cm squared paper.
On your diagram, plot the point D that makes a rectangle.
What are the coordinates of point D?

2 What is the area of each of these shapes made of rectangles?

a

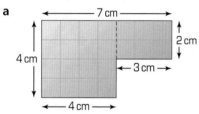

b

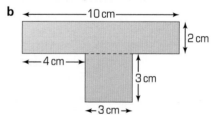

c

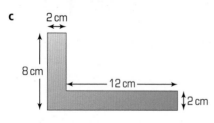

d

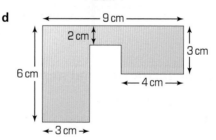

Number calculations

This unit will show you how to:

▶▶ Know what each digit represents in a number with up to 3 decimal places.

▶▶ Order a mixed set of numbers with up to 3 decimal places.

▶▶ Multiply and divide decimals by 10 and 100 and explain the effect.

▶▶ Round a number with up to 2 decimal places.

▶▶ Read measurements from scales.

▶▶ Consolidate mental addition and subtraction strategies.

▶▶ Use written methods.

▶▶ Partition numbers.

▶▶ Use informal pencil and paper methods to support, record or explain multiplications and divisions.

▶▶ Extend written methods to short multiplication of numbers involving decimals.

▶▶ Estimate by approximating, then check result.

▶▶ Derive quickly division facts corresponding to tables up to 10 × 10.

▶▶ Develop calculator skills and use a calculator effectively.

Multiplying and dividing are everyday skills.

Before you start

You should know how to ...

1 Order a mixed set of integers and fractions.

2 Find pairs of decimals that add to 1 or 10.

3 Multiply and divide any positive integer up to 10 000 by 10 and 100.

4 Know multiplication facts up to 10 × 10.

Check in

1 Order this set of numbers. Start with the smallest.
$7, 4\frac{1}{2}, 3\frac{3}{4}, 7\frac{1}{4}, 3, \frac{3}{4}, 4, 4\frac{1}{4}$

2 Copy and complete these calculations.
  a 0.7 + __ = 1   **b** 0.4 + __ = 1
  c 5.1 + __ = 10   **d** 3.2 + __ = 10

3 Work out:
  a 37 × 10   **b** 86 × 100
  c 40 ÷ 10   **d** 760 ÷ 100

4 Work out:
  a 2 × 5   **b** 7 × 0
  c 5 × 8   **d** 4 × 9

This spread will show you how to:

▶▶ Know what each digit represents in a number with up to 3 decimal places.
▶▶ Order numbers with up to 3 decimal places.

The red line is 3 cm long.

This means that it is 3 whole cm and no $\frac{1}{10}$'s cm.

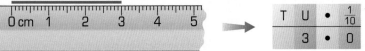

T	U	•	$\frac{1}{10}$
	3	•	0

This line is 2.7 cm long.
It is shorter than the 3 cm line.

This means that it is 2 whole cm and $\frac{7}{10}$ cm

T	U	•	$\frac{1}{10}$
	2	•	7

▶ To order numbers, start by comparing the largest place value of each number.

Even though 2.7 shows 7 in the $\frac{1}{10}$'s column, it only shows 2 in the units column, so 2.7 is smaller than 3 or 3.0.

▶ You can write 3.0 > 2.7 or 2.7 < 3.0.

example

Write these numbers in order from largest to smallest:
3.139, 2.397, 2.593, 2.511

Compare the largest
place value first: 3.139 is the largest.
Then look at the
next place value: 2.397 is the smallest as 3 < 5.
Then look at the
next place value: 2.593 > 2.511 as 9 > 1.
So the order is:
3.139, 2.593, 2.511, 2.397.

Exercise N2.1

1 Write down the positions of each of these arrows on this number line using decimals. Arrow F is at 3.2.

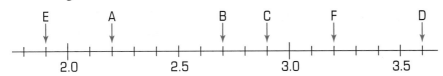

> Write to 1 decimal place.

2 Write these numbers as decimals.

a 1 unit and $\frac{3}{10}$ **b** 6 units and $\frac{8}{10}$ **c** 7 units and $\frac{1}{10}$

d 0 units and $\frac{9}{10}$ **e** 1 ten 3 units and $\frac{6}{10}$ **f** 2 tens 5 units and $\frac{5}{10}$

3 Use this place value table to re-write these numbers in order (smallest first).

10.0, 0.9, 5.2, 9.0, 6.1, 12.3, 8.3

T	U	•	$\frac{1}{10}$
1	0	•	0
	0	•	9
	5	•	2
	9	•	0
	6	•	1
1	2	•	3
	8	•	3

4 Use the correct sign (< or >) to order these pairs of decimal numbers.

a 4.0   0.4   **b** 0.8   2.1   **c** 0.7   1.0

d 10.01   0.12   **e** 1.03   0.71   **f** 2.32   0.95

g 1.5   2   **h** 0.8   1   **i** 12   1.2

j 6.32   0.85   **k** 0.7   9   **l** 9.8   10

> Remember:
> < means 'less than'.
> > means 'greater than'.

5 Estimate the decimal value for both arrows on each number line.

a 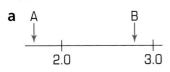   **b** 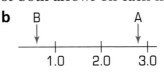   **c**

Estimate your answers to 1 decimal place.

This spread will show you how to:

▶▶ Multiply and divide decimals by 10 and 100 and explain the effect.

KEYWORDS

Digit

Decimal point

You can multiply or divide easily by 10 or 100.

▶ To multiply a number by 10, you move each digit 1 place to the left.

T	U	•	$\frac{1}{10}$	$\frac{1}{100}$
			8	9
2	8	•	9	

$2.89 \times 10 = 28.9$

▶ To divide a number by 10, you move each digit 1 place to the right.

T	U	•	$\frac{1}{10}$	$\frac{1}{100}$
1	9	•	9	
	1	•	9	9

$19.9 \div 10 = 1.99$

▶ To multiply a number by 100, you move each digit 2 places to the left.

H	T	U	•	$\frac{1}{10}$	$\frac{1}{100}$
		2	•	9	6
2	9	6	•		

$2.96 \times 100 = 296$

▶ To divide a number by 100, you move each digit 2 places to the right.

H	T	U	•	$\frac{1}{10}$	$\frac{1}{100}$
3	7	8	•		
		3	•	7	8

$378 \div 100 = 37.8$

Think about the digits changing place.
The decimal point and the place positions are fixed, they do not move.

▶ Sometimes you need to add 1 or more zeros to make the place positions right.

H	T	U	•	$\frac{1}{10}$	$\frac{1}{100}$	$\frac{1}{1000}$
		4	•	7	0	
4	7	0	•			

$4.70 \times 100 = 470$

H	T	U	•	$\frac{1}{10}$	$\frac{1}{100}$	$\frac{1}{1000}$
0	0	7	•	5		
		0	•	0	7	5

$7.5 \div 100 = 0.075$

Exercise N2.2

1 Write the answers to:
- **a** 5.7 × 10
- **b** 6.7 × 100
- **c** 4.1 × 10
- **d** 0.06 × 100
- **e** 15.3 × 10
- **f** 26.3 × 10
- **g** 13.7 × 100
- **h** 2.8 × 10
- **i** 12.9 × 10
- **j** 3.9 × 100
- **k** 1.3 × 100
- **l** 0.5 × 100

2 Write the answers to:
- **a** 21 ÷ 10
- **b** 67 ÷ 10
- **c** 56 ÷ 10
- **d** 92 ÷ 10
- **e** 157 ÷ 10
- **f** 304 ÷ 10
- **g** 177 ÷ 10
- **h** 330 ÷ 10
- **i** 17 ÷ 10
- **j** 36 ÷ 10
- **k** 447 ÷ 100
- **l** 500 ÷ 100

3 Write the answers to:
- **a** 34.32 ÷ 10
- **b** 76.83 ÷ 10
- **c** 91.22 ÷ 10
- **d** 59.44 ÷ 10
- **e** 46.55 ÷ 10
- **f** 37.32 ÷ 10
- **g** 1.87 ÷ 10
- **h** 3.93 ÷ 10
- **i** 566.5 ÷ 100
- **j** 297.3 ÷ 100
- **k** 16.87 ÷ 100
- **l** 3.93 ÷ 100

4 This is the answer displayed on Sarah's calculator.
Which of these calculations give this answer?

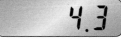

- **a** 43 ÷ 100
- **b** 0.34 × 10
- **c** 43 ÷ 10
- **d** 0.43 × 10
- **e** 430 ÷ 100

5 100 runners collected a total of £260 for charity.
Each person collected exactly the same amount of money.
How much did each runner collect?

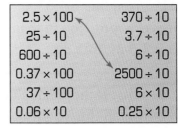

6 Match the pairs of calculations that are same.
Write out the calculations with the same answer.
The first one is done for you.

$$2.5 \times 100 \rightarrow 2500 \div 10$$

2.5 × 100	370 ÷ 10
25 ÷ 10	3.7 ÷ 10
600 ÷ 10	6 ÷ 10
0.37 × 100	2500 ÷ 10
37 ÷ 100	6 × 10
0.06 × 10	0.25 × 10

7 Harry has 0.5 kg of sweets to share between the 10 people
at his party. He shares them equally.
What weight of sweets does each person get?
- **a** Write your answer in kilograms.
- **b** Write your answer in grams.

This spread will show you how to:

▶▶ Round a number with up to 2 decimal places to the nearest tenth or to the nearest whole number.
▶▶ Read measurements from scales.

KEYWORDS
Round
Decimal

Rounding numbers makes it easier to calculate.

The red line is 10.6 cm long.
It can be rounded up to 11 cm to the nearest 1 cm.
It is closer to 11 cm than 10 cm.

▶ When a measurement is exactly half way between 2 units, you round up.

The blue line is 1.5 cm long.
To the nearest centimetre,
the line is 2 cm long.

The purple line is 1.13 m long.
It can be rounded to 1 m.

You can also round to 1 decimal place (dp).

The green line is 1.63 m long.
It is closer to 1.60 m than 1.70 m.
It is 1.6 m (to 1 dp).

example

a What is the reading on these scales?
b Round the weight to the nearest kg.
c Round the weight to 1 decimal place.

a The reading is 4.83 kg.
b The weight is 5 kg to the nearest kg.
c It is 4.8 kg to 1 dp.

Exercise N2.3

1 **a** How long are each of these lines?
b Round each measurement to the nearest centimetre.

i 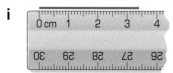 ii 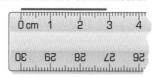 iii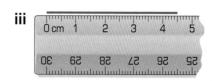

2 **a** How long are each of these lines?
b Round each measurement to the nearest metre.
c Round each measurement to 1 decimal place.

i  ii

iii

3 **a** What is the reading on each of these scales?
b Round each weight to the nearest kilogram.
c Round each weight to 1 decimal place.

i ii

iii

4 Round these amounts to the nearest whole number.
The first one is done for you.
a 8.2 cm = 8 cm (nearest 1 cm)
b 13.3 cm   **c** 9.1 kg   **d** 24.2 litres   **e** 31.8 tonnes   **f** 26.4 cm

5 Round this weight to the nearest whole kg.

1.5 kg

6 The table shows the heights of 5 boys.
a Round the heights to 1 decimal place.
b Which 2 boys are the same height when their heights are rounded?
c Whose height is 2.0 m when rounded?
d Whose height is 1 m when rounded to the nearest metre?

Name	Height in metres
Ben	1.72
Waleed	1.55
Ali	1.95
Scott	1.67
Roy	1.46

This spread will show you how to:

▶▶ Consolidate mental addition and subtraction strategies.
▶▶ Use written methods.

KEYWORDS
Partitioning
Compensate
Convert

You should be able to do most calculations in your head.
Here are 2 useful methods.

Partitioning

▶ 42 + 27
Break down 29 into 20 and 7 and
add on.

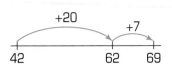

▶ 437 − 225
Break down 225 into 200, 20 and 5.

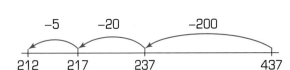

Compensation

▶ 42 + 29
Start from 42, add on 30.
Subtract 1 to compensate.

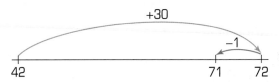

▶ 236 − 128
Start from 236, subtract 100, subtract 30.
Add 2.

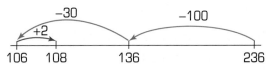

When you use a written method you line up the units.

example

Work out:

a £376 + £118

b £236 − £128

....

a
$$\begin{array}{r} 376 \\ +\,1\,1\,8 \\ \hline £\,4\,9\,4 \\ {}_{1} \end{array}$$
← 6 + 8 = 14

Keep the 4 in the units.
Include the 10 in the tens
addition.

b
$$\begin{array}{r} £\,2\,\overset{2}{\cancel{3}}\,\overset{1}{6} \\ -\,£\,1\,2\,8 \\ \hline £\,1\,0\,8 \end{array}$$

Taking 8 from 6 gives a
negative number, so
convert a ten into 10
units.
Put the 10 units into
the units place, then
subtract 8 from 16.

Exercise N2.4

1 Use a mental method to complete these additions and subtractions.

   a 43 + 36   **b** 53 + 24   **c** 71 + 25   **d** 132 + 44

   e 97 − 24   **f** 74 − 32   **g** 87 − 66   **h** 93 − 50

2 Use a mental method to complete these calculations.

   a 49 + 53   **b** 75 + 18   **c** 65 + 27   **d** 126 + 37

   e 91 − 45   **f** 57 − 39   **g** 84 − 37   **h** 135 − 29

   i 35 + 56   **j** 136 + 62   **k** 123 − 81   **l** 219 − 146

3 The diagram shows distances between junctions on a motorway.

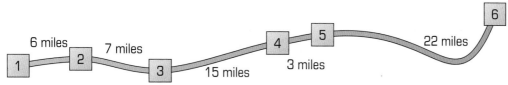

   a Which junction is 31 miles from junction 1?

   b If you are travelling from junction 6 to junction 2,
      how many miles is your journey?

4 The table shows the distances, in miles, between towns.

   a Which 2 towns are the nearest to each other?

   b How many miles is the journey from Bangor to Exeter?

   c How far is it from Exeter to Dover?

   d How far is the total journey from Bangor to Dover going by Exeter?

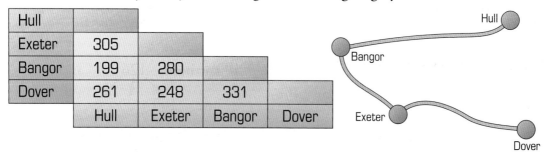

Hull			
Exeter	305		
Bangor	199	280	
Dover	261	248	331
	Hull	Exeter	Bangor	Dover

5 Pat has £396 in the bank. Ray has £57 less than Pat.
   How much does Ray have?

6 James weighs 68 kg, Mick weighs 81 kg and Steve weighs 56 kg.
   How much do they weigh altogether?
   Choose an answer from these totals.

   a 207   **b** 195   **c** 215   **d** 205   **e** 219

   Show how you would work this out using a written method.

This spread will show you how to:
- ▶▶ Consolidate knowing multiplication facts up to 10 × 10.
- ▶▶ Partition numbers.
- ▶▶ Use informal pencil and paper methods to support, record or explain multiplications.

KEYWORDS
Partition   Round
Compensation

You can multiply most numbers in your head if you know your multiplication facts.

4 × 29
Partition 29 to 20 + 9:
4 × 20 and 4 × 9
4 × 20 is 4 × 2 × 10 = 80.
4 × 9 = 36.
Now add: 36 + 80 = 116
The answer is 116.

4 × 29
Round 29 to 30.
4 × 30 is 4 × 3 × 10 = 12 × 10
4 × 30 = 120
Subtract 4 to compensate for rounding up to 30. The answer is 116.

Grids are useful for multiplying larger numbers.

example

Work out:
a 46 × 13.

b 126 × 47

a Partition   46 and 13
into   40 + 6 and 10 + 3.

Use the multiplication grid:

×	40	6
10	400	60
3	120	18

400 + 120 + 60 + 18 = 598
so   46 × 13 = 598

b Partition   126   and   47
into   100 + 20 + 6   40 + 7.

Use the multiplication grid:

×	100	20	6
40	4000	800	240
7	700	140	42

4000 + 700 + 800 + 140 + 240 + 42
= 5922
so 126 × 47 = 5922

Exercise N2.5

1 Test yourself. Write as many answers as you can in 3 minutes.

a 4×5	**b** 5×5	**c** 7×7	**d** 9×2	**e** 8×4
f 7×6	**g** 8×6	**h** 6×4	**i** 7×7	**j** 9×3
k 8×5	**l** 4×9	**m** 6×6	**n** 10×4	**o** 9×0
p 9×9	**q** 8×8	**r** 3×8	**s** 7×6	**t** 6×5

2 Choose the best approximate answer to these calculations.

a 48×4:   **i** 140   **ii** 300   **iii** 50   **iv** 200

b 72×8:   **i** 560   **ii** 720   **iii** 1000   **iv** 100

3 Do these multiplications mentally.

a $£32 \times 3 = £$___   **b** $13 \text{ kg} \times 6 = $ ___ kg   **c** $43 \text{ cm} \times 3 = $ ___ cm

d $22 \times 7 \, \ell = $ ___ ℓ **e** $8 \times 15 \text{ m} = $ ___ m   **f** $34 \text{ mm} \times 6 = $ ___ mm

4 Each of these pipes is 38 cm long.

38 cm

When all 5 pipes are joined end to end, what is the total length?
Work out the answer mentally.

5 Use a written method to do these calculations. The first one is started for you.

a 64×7

×	60	4
7	420	28

$64 \times 7 = $ ___ + ___

b 33×7 **c** 51×7 **d** 34×8

e 5×27 **f** 69×4 **g** 47×8

6 Use a written method to do these calculations. The first one is started for you.

a 32×12

×	30	2
10	300	20
2	60	4

$32 \times 12 = $ ___ + ___ + ___ + ___

b 34×15 **c** 25×17 **d** 29×14

e 52×16 **f** 75×16 **g** 18×18

7 Use a written method to do these calculations. The first one is started for you.

a 176×23

×	100	70	6
20	2000	1400	120
3	300	210	18

$176 \times 23 = $ ___ + ___ + ___ + ___ + ___ + ___

b $321 \times 17 = $ **c** $293 \times 13 = $ **f** $423 \times 38 = $

This spread will show you how to:

▶▶ Extend written methods to short multiplication of numbers involving decimals.

▶▶ Estimate by approximating, then check results.

KEYWORDS

Approximate   Factor

Accurate   Partition

Each of these 6 pipes is 1.9 m long.

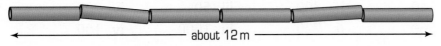

about 12 m

When they are joined end to end the total length is 1.9×6.
Each pipe is approximately 2 m long, so the total length is about 12 m.

You can calculate the exact length of the pipes mentally.
Think of the calculation like this: 19×6
                 Partition 19 into $10 + 9$
                      $10 \times 6 = 60$ and $9 \times 6 = 54$
                  So $19 \times 6 = 60 + 54$
                          $= 114$

You could work out:
$20 \times 6 = 120$
$120 - 6 = 114$

You know that the answer is about 12.
So $1.9 \times 6 = 11.4$ m

▶ **To multiply a number by 10, you move the digits 1 place to the left.**

$1.9 \times 10 = 19$
so $1.9 \times 20 = 1.9 \times 10 \times 2$
          $= 19 \times 2$
          $= 38$

example

Work out:

a 2.8×7

b 2.6×30

....

a Treat 2.8 as 28

Partition 28 into $20 + 8$

×	20	8
7	140	56

$28 \times 7 = 140 + 56 = 196$
An approximate answer is $3 \times 7 = 21$.
The accurate answer is 19.6

b Break 30 into factors:

$30 = 10 \times 3$

So $2.6 \times 30 = 2.6 \times 10 \times 3$
          $= 26 \times 3$
          $= 78$

Exercise N2.6

1 Copy and complete these multiplications.

   a 4.5×10 **b** 5.3×10 **c** 1.2×10

   d 7.7×10 **e** 9.8×10 **f** 10×5.1

   g 12.3×10 **h** 10×21.7 **i** 7.9×10

   j 8.6×10 **k** 23.7×10 **l** 10×31.9

> This place value table may help you:
>
> | H | T | U | • | $\frac{1}{10}$ |
> |---|---|---|---|---|

2 Copy and complete these calculations. The first one has been done for you.

   a $3.3 \times 20 = 3.3 \times 10 \times 2$
                $= 33 \times 2$
                $= 66$

   b $5.7 \times 20 = 5.7 \times 10 \times \underline{\ \ }$
                $= 57 \times \underline{\ \ }$
                $= \underline{\ \ }$

   c $2.9 \times 30 = 2.9 \times \underline{\ \ } \times \underline{\ \ }$
                $= \underline{\ \ } \times \underline{\ \ }$

   d $4.3 \times 40 =$

   e $5.8 \times 20 =$ **f** $3.9 \times 50 =$

3 The length of one of these tiles is 15.4 cm.
When 20 tiles are laid out in a straight line how far will they stretch?

This calculation will help you.
$15.4 \times 20 = 15.4 \times \underline{\ \ } \times \underline{\ \ }$
          $= \underline{\ \ } \times \underline{\ \ }$
          $= \underline{\ \ }$ cm

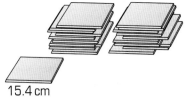

15.4 cm

4 Use grids to partition these multiplications.
Remember to make an approximation first.

   a 1.7×8
      Treat 1.7 as 17

×	10	7
8	80	56

1.7 is nearly 2. $2 \times 8 = 16$
So the answer is about 16.
   $17 \times 8 = 80 + 56 = \underline{\ \ }$
So $1.7 \times 8 = \underline{\ \ }\ \underline{\ \ } . \underline{\ \ }$

   b 2.8×6

×	20	8
6	?	?

2.8 is approximately 3.

   c 4.8×9 (Treat 4.8 as 48. 4.8 is approximately 5)

   d $3.6 \times 7 =$ **e** $2.7 \times 5 =$ **f** $3.8 \times 6 =$

5 This parcel weighs 6.2 kg.
How much will 9 identical parcels weigh?

This spread will show you how to:
- ▶▶ Derive quickly division facts corresponding to tables up to 10 × 10.
- ▶▶ Break a number into factors.
- ▶▶ Use informal pencil and paper methods to support, record or explain divisions.

To work out 900 ÷ 30
you can break 30 into factors 10 × 3.
You divide by 10, then you divide by 3:
900 ÷ 10 = 90
90 ÷ 3 = 30

or … you can divide by 3
and then divide by 10.
900 ÷ 3 = 300
300 ÷ 10 = 30

Another mental method is to keep subtracting 30.
900 − 30 = 270
270 − 30 = 240
240 − 30 = 210…
This will take a long time!

You can subtract 'chunks' of 30.
A chunk of ten 30's is 300.
900 − 300 = 600 … 10 × 30
600 − 300 = 300 … another 10 × 30
300 − 300 = 0 … another 10 × 30
So 900 ÷ 30 = 30 (10 + 10 + 10).

example

How many groups of 16 can you make from 107?

107 − 16 = 91 … 1 × 16
91 − 16 = 75 … 2 × 16
75 − 16 = 59 … 3 × 16
59 − 16 = 43 … 4 × 16
43 − 16 = 27 … 5 × 16
27 − 16 = 11 … 6 × 16
There are 6 groups of 16 in 107 with 11 left over.

To make the calculation quicker, 'chunk' together the groups of 16 into chunks of 32.
107 − 32 = 75 … 2 × 16
75 − 32 = 43 … 4 × 16
43 − 32 = 11 … 6 × 16
There are 6 groups of 16 in 107 and there are 11 left over.

You can use larger chunks.
Try chunks of 48 because 48 = 3 × 16.

Exercise N2.7

1 Test yourself. Write as many answers as you can in 5 minutes.

   a $12 \div 6$ **b** $12 \div 4$ **c** $18 \div 3$ **d** $25 \div 5$

   e $35 \div 7$ **f** $40 \div 8$ **g** $36 \div 4$ **h** $24 \div 8$

   i $56 \div 7$ **j** $72 \div 9$ **k** $81 \div 9$ **l** $27 \div 3$

2 Copy and complete these calculations.

   a $16 \times \underline{} = 32$ **b** $3 \times \underline{} = 45$ **c** $15 \times \underline{} = 60$

   d $48 \div \underline{} = 16$ **e** $70 \div \underline{} = 10$ **f** $80 \div \underline{} = 20$

3 Use breaking into factors to complete these divisions.
The first one is done for you.

   a $600 \div 15$ $(15 = 3 \times 5)$

      $600 \div 3 = 200$ $200 \div 5 = 40$

      So $600 \div 15 = 40$

   b $900 \div 15$ $(15 = 3 \times 5)$ **c** $560 \div 35$ $(35 = 7 \times 5)$

   d $450 \div 30$ $(30 = 10 \times 3)$ **e** $640 \div 40$ $(40 = 10 \times 4)$

   f $720 \div 120$ $(120 = 10 \times 2 \times 6)$ **g** $840 \div 24$ $(24 = 2 \times 2 \times 2 \times 3)$

4 Emma takes part in a 180 km canoe race. The race has 15 equal stages.
How long is each stage of the race?

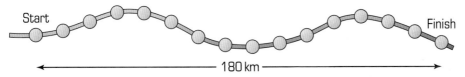

5 Use 'chunking' to divide these numbers.

   a $299 \div 13$ Hint: you can chunk with 26: (2×13) or 130: (10×13)

   b $163 \div 14$ Hint: there is a remainder.

   c $371 \div 18$ Hint: there is a remainder.

   d $196 \div 14$

6 Use chunking to solve this problem.
The Navy uses 3 helicopters to rescue people at sea.
The helicopters can each carry 6 passengers.

How many trips will the helicopters have to make to
rescue 153 people from a sinking ship?

This spread will show you how to:
▶▶ Develop calculator skills and use a calculator effectively.
▶▶ Choose and use appropriate number operations to solve problems.

KEYWORDS
Solve
Problem

Calculators do not think for you.
They just do the calculations you give to them.

example

To calculate the distance from Brighton to Kingston, which calculation will you use?

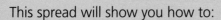

a 28 − 27 miles   **b** 27 − 28 miles
c 28 × 27 miles   **d** 28 + 27 miles

Brighton 28 m   Kingston 27 m

The correct solution is 28 + 27 miles.

Calculators do not know about money.
You have to be careful when calculating money problems.

£4.57   +   £9·73

The total on these 2 price tags is

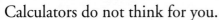

4 · 5 7 + 9 · 7 3 = 14.3

You need to know what 14.3 means to give a full answer.
In money, 14.3 means £14.30.
You also need to remember to make sure all quantities are in the same units.

You can do this calculation using the memory button:
    650 ÷ (57 − 44).
The brackets tell you to subtract 57 − 44 first.

You can then store the answer in the memory.

5 7 − 4 4 = 13 → Enter into memory M+

Then you can enter 650 and divide it by the number in the memory.

6 5 0 ÷ MR = 50

Exercise N2.8

1 12 jars of coffee cost £11.64.
Which of these calculations do you use to find the
cost of 1 jar?

  a 11.64 − 12   **b** 12 + 11.64

  c 11.64 ÷ 12   **d** 11.64 × 12

2 This table shows the number of white and brown loaves
that a baker sold in a week.

	Mon	Tue	Wed	Thur	Fri	Sat
Brown loaves	225	175	173	274	202	227
White loaves	121	210	182	97	159	89

  a How much brown bread was sold altogether?

  b How much more brown bread than white bread was sold?

  c On which day was the least bread sold?

3 Work out these. Give full answers.

  a £3.27 + £9.53   **b** £23.92 − £5.90

  c £256 ÷ 4   **d** £150 ÷ 4

  e £12.90 × 12   **f** £18.50 − £12.45

> Remember the £ sign.

4 The cost of renting a television is £2.89 per week.
How much would you pay if you rented the television
for 2 years?

5 Use the memory button on your calculator to do
these calculations.

  a 32 × (225 ÷ 15)   **b** 1.5 × (81 − 68)   **c** 183 + (5.6 × 5)

  d 25 ÷ (4.5 ÷ 9)   **e** £75 − (£6.20 × 5)   **f** 295 ÷ (3.7 + 6.3)

6 A pilot flies from A to F.
She has enough fuel to fly 1100 miles
List the routes that she can take.

You could start:

A → B → ...   409 miles + ...

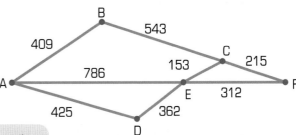

> All distances are in miles.

You should know how to ...

1 Order a mixed set of numbers with up to 3 decimal places.

2 Add and subtract decimals.

3 Multiply and divide decimals by 10 and 100 and explain the effect.

4 Extend written methods to short multiplication of numbers involving decimals.

5 Derive quickly division facts corresponding to tables up to 10 × 10.

Check out

1 Order this set of numbers.
Start with the smallest.

6, 5.5, 5, 6.4, 6.3, 5.66, 5.9

2 Work out these additions and subtractions:

a 0.3 + 0.6	**b** 1.1 + 0.8
c 1.4 + 0.6	**d** 3.4 + 0.7
e 2.8 − 0.8	**f** 4.9 − 0.5
g 3.7 − 1.4	**h** 1.1 − 0.8

3 Work out these multiplications and divisions:

a 3.4 × 10	**b** 6.22 × 10
c 0.75 × 100	**d** 1.2 × 100
e 9.2 ÷ 10	**f** 8.22 ÷ 10
g 52.3 ÷ 100	**h** 40 ÷ 100

4 Work out these multiplications.

a 1.1 × 6

b 4.2 × 3

c 1.7 × 4

d 3.5 × 7

5 Copy and complete these calculations:

a 9 × __ = 54	**b** 7 × __ = 14
c 4 × __ = 12	**d** 40 ÷ 8 = __
e 32 ÷ 4 = __	**f** 63 ÷ 7 = __

This unit will show you how to:

▶▶ Find common multiples.

▶▶ Recognise prime numbers to at least 20.

▶▶ Factorise numbers up to 100 into prime factors.

▶▶ Order a set of positive and negative numbers.

▶▶ Find the difference between a positive and a negative number.

▶▶ Construct and solve simple linear equations.

▶▶ Substitute positive integers into simple linear equations.

▶▶ Generate coordinate pairs that satisfy a simple linear rule.

▶▶ Plot graphs of simple linear functions.

▶▶ Express simple functions using symbols.

▶▶ Recognise straight-line graphs parallel to the x-axis or y-axis.

▶▶ Begin to plot and interpret graphs arising from real-life situations.

▶▶ Solve a problem by interpreting graphs.

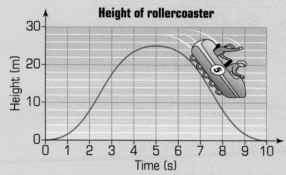

Height of rollercoaster

Height (m) / Time (s)

You can use graphs to describe many different functions.

Before you start

You should know how to ...

1 Compare numbers.
  ▶ > means greater than: 6 > 1
  ▶ < means less than: 2 < 7

2 Use function machines.

3 Plot coordinates.

Check in

1 Write the symbol to make these statements correct. Choose from <, > or =

  a 9 __ 6   **b** 8 − 2 __ 7 + 1

  c 7 − 4 __ 4 − 1   **d** ⁻1 __ 0

2 Copy and complete this table for each of these function machines.

Input	2	5	7	9
Output				

  a → ×6 →   **b** → + 7 →

3 Plot these coordinates on a squared grid.
  (⁻3, ⁻2) (⁻1, 1) (4, 1) (2, ⁻2)
  What shape have you drawn?

This spread will show you how to:
▶▶ Recognise multiples up to 10 × 10.
▶▶ Find common multiples.
▶▶ Factorise numbers up to 100.

KEYWORDS
Factor
Multiple
Lowest common multiple

The numbers in the table are all multiples.

×	1	2	3	4	5	6	7
1	1	2	3	4	5	6	7
2	2	4	6	8	10	12	14
3	3	6	9	12	15	18	21
4	4	8	12	16	20	24	28
5	5	10	15	20	25	30	35
6	6	12	18	24	30	36	42
7	7	14	21	28	35	42	49

Even though you cannot see the number 120, it is a multiple of 6.
$$120 = 60 \times 2$$
and $60 = 10 \times 6$.

▶ A multiple of 6 is any number in the 6 times table.

The multiples of 4 are 4, 8, ⑫, 16, 20, 24, …

The multiples of 6 are 6, ⑫, 18, 24, …

The numbers 4 and 6 have common multiples.
You can see that they share the multiples 12 and 24.
The **lowest common multiple** is 12.

▶ A factor of 16 is any number that divides into 16 exactly.

In the table you can see some factors of 16:
    $16 = 4 \times 4$
or $16 = 2 \times 8$
or $16 = 1 \times 16$

The factor pairs of 16 are:
1 and 16,   2 and 8,   4 and 4

×	1	2	3	4	5	6
1	1	2	3	4	5	6
2	2	4	6	8	10	12
3	3	6	9	12	15	18
4	4	8	12	16	20	24
5	5	10	15	20	25	30
6	6	12	18	24	30	36
7	7	14	21	28	35	42
8	8	16	24	32	40	48

Exercise A4.1

1 List as many factor pairs as you can for these numbers.
The first one is done for you.

a 15: 1 and 15, 3 and 5

b 20   **c** 18
d 24   **e** 36
f 60   **g** 100

2 List the first 5 multiples of these numbers.
The first one is done for you.

a 7: 7, 14, 28, 49, 56

b 3   **c** 6
d 9   **e** 4

3 Find the lowest common multiple of these numbers.
The first one is done for you.

a 5 and 8   5: 5, 10, 15, 20, 25, 30, 35, (40), 45

                    8: 8, 16, 24, 32, (40), 48

The lowest common multiple is 40.

b 6 and 9   **c** 3 and 9   **d** 4 and 7   **e** 6 and 7

4 Which of these numbers are multiples of 10?
   a 15   **b** 30   **c** 62   **d** 1290   **e** 2031   **f** 10 290

5 Explain how you can easily recognise a number that is a multiple of 10.

6 All of these numbers are multiples of 3.

Number	Digits		Total
45	4	5	9
63	6	3	
24	2	4	
57	5	7	
42	4	2	

a Copy and complete the table by adding together the digits of each number.
b The totals of the digits are multiples of which number?
c Which of these numbers are multiples of 3?
    72   62   55   54   81   108   225

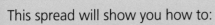

This spread will show you how to:

▶▶ Recognise prime numbers to at least 20.
▶▶ Factorise numbers up to 100 into prime factors.

KEYWORDS
Prime numbers
Prime factors

12 CDs can be arranged in 6 different ways, because 12 has 6 factors:

2×6 or 6×2

3×4 or 4×3

12×1 or 1×12

There are only 2 ways to arrange 3 CDs:
3 has only 2 factors.

3×1 or 1×3

There are only 2 ways to arrange 5 CDs:
5 has only 2 factors.

5×1 or 1×5

▶ Numbers with only 2 factors are called **prime numbers**.
3 and 5 are prime numbers.

A prime number divides evenly only by 1 and itself.

You can break a number down into prime factors.

example

a Break down 12 into its prime factors.   **b** Break down 30 into its prime factors.

a

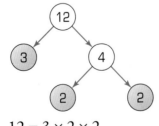

$12 = 3 \times 2 \times 2$

b

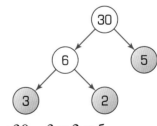

$30 = 3 \times 2 \times 5$

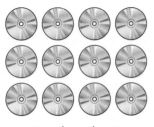

Exercise A4.2

1 Draw some ways to arrange these numbers of counters.
The first one is done for you.

   a 10 counters
      There are 4 ways:

5×2 or 2×5

10×1 or 1×10

   b 14 counters   **c** 20 counters   **d** 18 counters   **e** 32 counters

2 Which of these numbers are prime?

   a 11   **b** 9   **c** 13

> Think of re-arranging into rectangles.

3 Use this table to help you to decide which of these numbers are prime.

> Remember that prime numbers can only be arranged in 2 ways.

×	1	2	3	4	5	6	7
1	1	2	3	4	5	6	7
2	2	4	6	8	10	12	14
3	3	6	9	12	15	18	21
4	4	8	12	16	20	24	28
5	5	10	15	20	25	30	35
6	6	12	18	24	30	36	42
7	7	14	21	28	35	42	49

   a 18   **b** 31   **c** 17   **d** 35

4 Copy and complete the diagrams to find the prime factors of these numbers.

   a 18   **b** 36   **c** 60

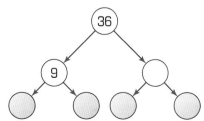
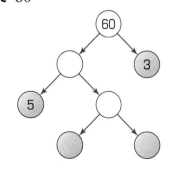

5 Break down 45 into its prime factors.

This spread will show you how to:

▶▶ Order a set of positive and negative numbers.
▶▶ Find the difference between a positive and a negative number.

KEYWORDS
Positive   Negative
Add   Subtract

This thermometer shows positive and negative numbers.

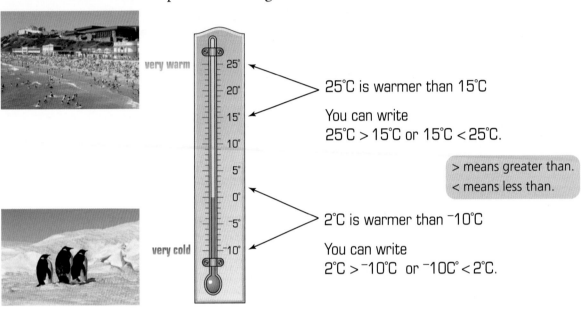

very warm

25°C is warmer than 15°C

You can write
25°C > 15°C or 15°C < 25°C.

> means greater than.
< means less than.

2°C is warmer than ⁻10°C

very cold

You can write
2°C > ⁻10°C or ⁻10C° < 2°C.

▶ You can use a number line to add and subtract positive and negative numbers.

example

Work out: **a** ⁻4 + 7   **b** ⁻1 − 5

....

a Start at ⁻4 → add on 7 → the answer is 3.

⁻4 + 7 = 3   ⁻4   +7   3

$$-5 \quad -4 \quad -3 \quad -2 \quad -1 \quad 0 \quad 1 \quad 2 \quad 3 \quad 4 \quad 5 \quad 6$$

b The answer is ⁻6. ← subtract 5 ← Start at ⁻1

⁻1 − 5 = ⁻6   ⁻6   −5   ⁻1

$$-7 \quad -6 \quad -5 \quad -4 \quad -3 \quad -2 \quad -1 \quad 0 \quad 1 \quad 2 \quad 3 \quad 4$$

Exercise A4.3

1 Order each set of temperatures from the highest to the lowest.

    a 3°, ⁻3°, 1°, ⁻4°   **b** ⁻1°, ⁻20°, 0°, ⁻6°

    c 8°, 7°, ⁻2°, ⁻12°   **d** 5°, 0°, 1°, 10°

2 Use 'more than' and 'less than' signs (> and <) to order
these numbers.

    The first one is done for you.

    a ⁻4 > ⁻7   **b** 8 10   **c** 2 ⁻5   **d** ⁻8 0

    e ⁻4 2   **f** ⁻2 ⁻1   **g** ⁻5 ⁻9   **h** ⁻3 ⁻4

3 Copy and complete these calculations. The number line can help you.

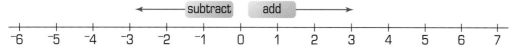

    a 3 + 4   **b** ⁻2 + 2   **c** ⁻6 + 9 + 2

    d 2 − 8   **e** ⁻3 − 2   **f** ⁻5 + 4

    g ⁻1 − 4   **h** ⁻6 + 2   **i** 5 − 6 − 2

4 This is a number 'story'.

    ▶ At breakfast time the temperature was ⁻6 °C.

    ▶ By lunch time it had risen by 11°.

    ▶ The temperature is now 5°.

    The story can be written as a calculation: ⁻6 + 11 = 5.

    Write these stories as calculations and work out the answers.

    a At midnight the temperature was ⁻3 °C.

       By 8 am the temperature had risen by 12°.

    b The lift was at floor ⁻8.

       The lift rose by 7 floors.

5 Copy and complete these 2 magic squares.
The totals of the rows and the columns and the diagonals
are all the same.

a

8	?	6
?	5	?
4	9	2

b

⁻2	?	?
3	1	?
2	?	4

A4.4 Trial and improvement

This spread will show you how to:

▶▶ Solve mathematical problems and puzzles.
▶▶ Construct and solve simple linear equations.
▶▶ Substitute positive integers into simple linear equations.

KEYWORDS
Solve
Equation

These scales balance.
You can write the picture as an equation:

$$4c + 15 = 25 + 2c$$

c stands for the weight of a tin.

To find the weight of a tin you can use trial and improvement.

This means trying different values in your equation to see if the sides balance.

Begin by trying 1 kg for the weight of a tin: $c = 1$.

The left and right do not balance.

The 2 answers are becoming closer.

c	Left side of balance			Right side of balance		
	$4 \times c$	+15	Answer	$2 \times c$	+25	Answer
1	$4 \times 1 = 4$	+15	19	$2 \times 1 = 2$	+25	27
2	$4 \times 2 = 8$	+15	23	$2 \times 2 = 4$	+25	29
3	$4 \times 3 = 12$	+15	27	$2 \times 3 = 6$	+25	31
4	$4 \times 4 = 16$	+15	31	$2 \times 4 = 8$	+25	33
5	$4 \times 5 = 24$	+15	35	$2 \times 5 = 10$	+25	35

The sides balance when the weight is 5 so the weight of a tin must be 5 kg.

You can write your calculations in a table or you can use jottings like these:

Try $c = 1$ $4 \times 1 = 4$ and $4 + 15 = 19$ $2 \times 1 = 2$ and $2 + 25 = 27$ not equal
Try $c = 2$ $4 \times 2 = 8$ and $8 + 15 = 23$ $2 \times 2 = 4$ and $4 + 25 = 29$ not equal
Try $c = 3$ $4 \times 3 = 12$ and $12 + 15 = 27$ $2 \times 3 = 6$ and $6 + 25 = 31$ not equal
Try $c = 4$ $4 \times 4 = 16$ and $16 + 15 = 31$ $2 \times 4 = 8$ and $8 + 25 = 33$ not equal
Try $c = 5$ $4 \times 5 = 20$ and $20 + 15 = 35$ $2 \times 5 = 10$ and $10 + 25 = 35$ equal ✓

So the weight of a can is 5 kg.

Exercise A4.4

1 Use trial and improvement to solve the equations for these balances.

   a $2c + 9 = 5 + 4c$ **b** $3c + 12 = 17 + 2c$

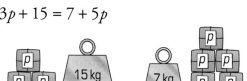 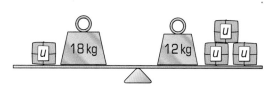

   c $3p + 15 = 7 + 5p$ **d** $u + 18 = 12 + 3u$

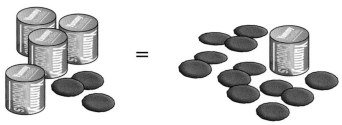

2 Find the number that makes the left side of this equation
   balance with the right side.
   Copy and complete the table to help you.

   left side   right side
   $4c + 8 \quad = \quad 9c - 7$

c	4 × c	+8	Answer	9 × c	−7	Answer
1	4 × 1 = 4	+8	12	9 × 1 = 9	−7	2

3 Find the number that balances this equation.
   Copy and complete the table to help you

   left side   right side
   $7n + 9 \quad = \quad n + 33$

n	7 × n	+9	Answer	n	+33	Answer
1	7 × 1 = 7	+9	16	1	+33	34

4 Solve these equations using trial and improvement.

   a $4x + 15 = 9x + 5$ **b** $10m - 6 = 4m + 24$ **c** $7t + 3 = 4t + 6$
   d $6y - 2 = 2y + 6$ **e** $20h - 12 = 10h + 28$ **f** $8w - 5 = 6w + 3$

5 a Write the equation for this picture.
   b Use trial and improvement to find the number of biscuits in a packet.

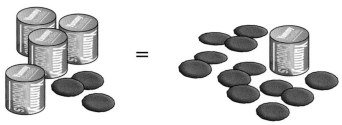

This spread will show you how to:

▶▶ Generate coordinate pairs that satisfy a simple linear rule.
▶▶ Plot the graphs of simple linear functions.
▶▶ Recognise and explain patterns and relationships.

KEYWORDS

Variable   Grid
x-axis   *y*-axis
Table of values
Coordinates
Straight-line graph
x-coordinate
y-coordinate

This equation shows the relationship between 2 numbers, *x* and *y*.

$$y = x - 2$$

x and *y* are called variables because they can change.

The table shows how they change in this equation:
The *y* variable is the *x* variable minus 2.

x	⁻2	⁻1	0	1	2	3	4
−2	−2	−2	−2	−2	−2	−2	−2
y	⁻4	⁻3	⁻2	⁻1	0	1	2

You can read the
pairs of values (*x, y*):   (⁻2, ⁻4) (⁻1, ⁻3) (0, ⁻2)

▶ You can plot coordinate pairs on a grid.
The *x*-axis is horizontal. The *y*-axis is vertical.

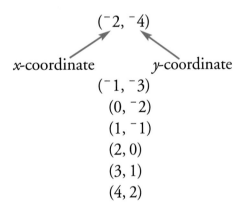

(⁻2, ⁻4)

x-coordinate   *y*-coordinate

(⁻1, ⁻3)
(0, ⁻2)
(1, ⁻1)
(2, 0)
(3, 1)
(4, 2)

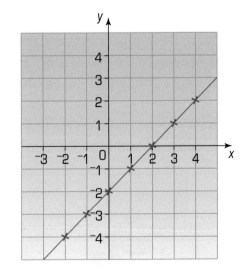

The coordinate pairs make a straight line because they come from the same equation, *y* = *x* − 2.

Exercise A4.5

1 Copy and complete the table of values for each of these equations.

a $y = x + 3$

x	-2	-1	0	1	2	3	4
	+3	+3		+3			+3
y	1			4			

b $y = x - 2$

x	-1	0	1	2	3	4	5
	-2				-2		
y					1		

c $y = x$

x	-2	-1	0	1	2	3	4
y			0				

2 a Write the coordinate pairs for each table in question 1.

b Copy these axes and plot the coordinate pairs for each equation.
Label each line clearly.

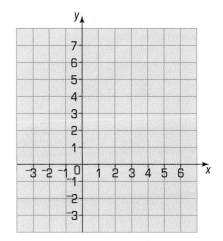

3 a Copy and complete this table of values for the equation $y = x - 3$. The x values are from ⁻1 to 10.

x	-1	0	1	2	3	4	5	6	7	8	9	10
	-3	-3	-3	-3	-3	-3	-3	-3	-3	-3	-3	-3
y												

b Draw axes like these.

c Plot the x and y coordinates to make a straight line.

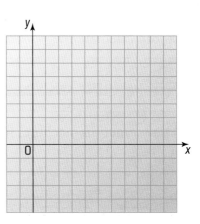

4 Use axes as in question 3 to draw the line of the equation $y = x + 1$ for x values from ⁻1 to 5.

This spread will show you how to:

▶▶ Generate coordinate pairs that satisfy a simple linear rule.
▶▶ Plot the graphs of simple linear functions.
▶▶ Express simple functions using symbols.
▶▶ Recognise and explain patterns and relationships.

KEYWORDS

Equation   Coordinates
Variable

The coordinates on this line are:
($^-$4, $^-$4) ($^-$3, $^-$3) ($^-$2, $^-$2) ($^-$1, $^-$1)
(0, 0) (1, 1) (2, 2) (3, 3) (4, 4)

The y-coordinate and the x-coordinate always have the same value.

y-coordinate = x-coordinate.

The equation of the line is $y = x$.

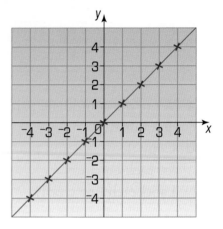

▶ The equation is the rule that links the x and y variables.

The coordinates of this line are:
(0, 0) (1, 2) (2, 4) (3, 6) (4, 8) (5, 10)

The y-coordinate is double the x-coordinate.

y-coordinate = 2 × x-coordinate

The equation of the line is $y = 2x$.

$x \longrightarrow \boxed{\times 2} \Longrightarrow y$

You can calculate the y-coordinates in a table.

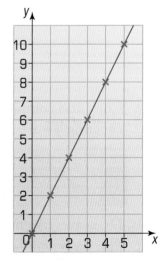

x	0	1	2	3	4	5
y	2×0=0	2×1=2	2×2=4	2×3=6	2×4=8	2×5=10

example

Draw function machines for these equations:

a $y = x - 2$ **b** $y = \frac{1}{4}x$

....

a $x \longrightarrow \boxed{-2} \Longrightarrow y$ **b** $x \longrightarrow \boxed{\div 4} \Longrightarrow y$

Exercise A4.6

1 Copy and complete the tables of values for these equations.

a $y = 3x$

x	−1	0	1	2	3	4
y	−3		3			

b $y = \frac{1}{2}x$

x	−2	0	2	4	6	8
y		0	1			

c $y = x + 2$

x	−2	0	2	4	6	8
y	0	2				

2 **a** Copy these axes.
   b Plot all the sets of points from question 1.
   c Join the points to make sure that they make straight lines.
   d Suggest some more coordinate pairs that you cannot see but you think would be on each line.

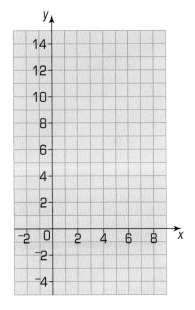

3 **a** Write down the marked sets of coordinates for each line.
   b From the coordinates, work out the equation of each line.
   Here is how to start line A:
   ▸ The coordinates are (1, 5) and (2, 10).
   ▸ The y-coordinate is 5 times the x-coordinate.
   ▸ So $y = \_\_ \times x$
   or $y = \_\_ x$

   > You can make equations with +, −, × or ÷.

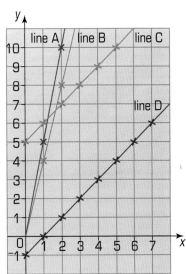

4 Which of these coordinates will be on the line $y = 6x$?
   (2, 3) (6, 1) (1, 6) (2, 12) (30, 5) (5, 30)

This spread will show you how to:

▶▶ Generate coordinate pairs that satisfy a simple linear rule.
▶▶ Plot the graphs of simple linear functions.
▶▶ Recognise and explain patterns and relationships.

Sian used this rule to do her calculations:

$x \longrightarrow \boxed{\times 2} \Longrightarrow \boxed{+ 1} \Longrightarrow y$

The rule is made from more than 1 operation.
The input is x and the output is y.

You can use these function machines to find coordinate pairs.

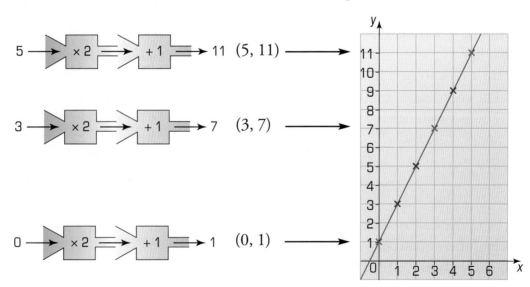

Exercise A4.7

1 a Use this machine to calculate the *y*-coordinates for these *x*-coordinates.
  b Copy the table and write in your *y*-coordinates.

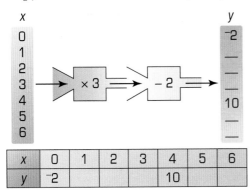

x	0	1	2	3	4	5	6
y	-2				10		

2 For the equation $y = 2x - 1$:
  a Write the 2 rules into a copy of this machine in the correct order.

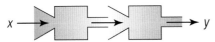

  b Copy and complete this table of values using the rule.

x	0	1	2	3	4	5	6
y	-1			5			

3 The equation $y = 3x + 1$ uses 2 operations.
  a Draw the function machines for the equation.
  b Copy and complete this table of values.

x	0	1	2	3	4	5
y	1	4				

  c Plot the *x*- and *y*-coordinates on a copy of these axes.
  d Check that they make a straight line.

4 Repeat question 3 for the equation $y = 4x - 3$.

5 Which of these coordinates will be on the line of the equation $y = 3x + 1$?
  (0, 1) (3, 8) (5, 16) (10, 31)

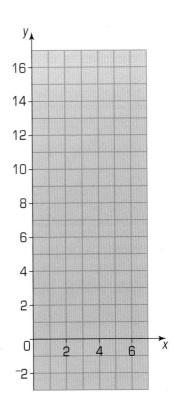

This spread will show you how to:
▶▶ Express simple functions in symbols.
▶▶ Recognise straight-line graphs parallel to an axis.
▶▶ Recognise and explain patterns and relationships.

KEYWORDS
Coordinates
Straight-line graph
Parallel

Here is a set of coordinates.
($^-$2, 3) (0, 3) (2, 3) (5, 3) (7, 3)
They join to make a straight line.

The line is **parallel** to the x-axis.

All the points on the line have a
y-coordinate of 3.

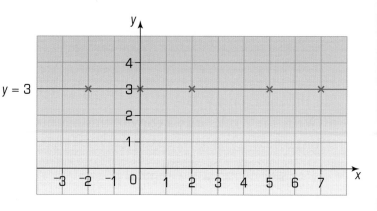

$y = 3$

▶ You call the line $y = 3$.

The coordinates of the blue line are:
($^-$2, $^-$2) ($^-$2, 0) ($^-$2, 1) ($^-$2, 4) ($^-$2, 7)

They all have the same x value.

The coordinates all join to make a straight line.

All the points on the line have an x-coordinate
of $^-$2.

▶ You call the line $x = {^-}2$.

$x = {^-}2$ is parallel to the y-axis.

Here are the coordinates of the red line:
(3, $^-$2) (3, 0) (3, 1) (3, 4) (3, 7)

They all have the same x-coordinate: 3.

▶ You call the line $x = 3$.

$x = 3$ is parallel to the y-axis.

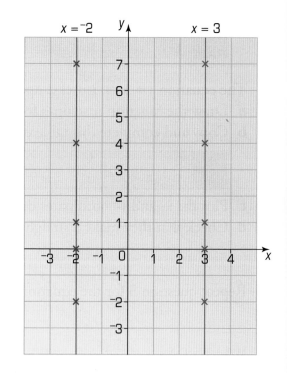

1 Write the names of each of the lines on the grid.
The first one has been done for you.

Line a: $x = {}^-9$

Line b:

Line c:

Line d:

Line e:

Line f:

Line g:

Line h:

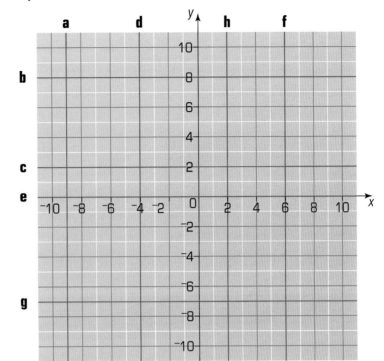

2 a Copy these axes and plot these sets of
coordinates.
Line 1: $({}^-1, 4)$ $(2, 4)$ $(7, 4)$
Line 2: $({}^-2, 0)$ $({}^-2, 3)$ $({}^-2, 5)$
Line 3: $(6, 0)$ $(6, 4)$ $(6, 5)$
b Write the name of each line.
c Write the coordinates where lines 1
and 3 cross each other.

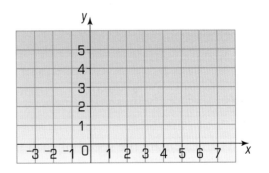

3 a Without drawing these lines, write their names:
Line A: $({}^-2, 10)$ $(7, 10)$ $(15, 10)$
Line B: $(3, {}^-4)$ $(3, 3)$ $(3, 13)$

Intersect means cross.

b What are the coordinates of the point where the 2 lines intersect?

4 a Write another description for the line $y = 0$.
b Write another description for the line $x = 0$.

This spread will show you how to:

▶▶ Begin to plot and interpret graphs arising from real-life situations.
▶▶ Solve a problem by interpreting graphs.

KEYWORDS

Speed   Horizontal
km/h   Vertical

This is a cyclist's race route.
Each lap of the route is 10 km.

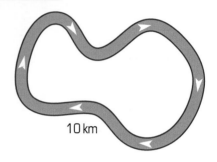

10 km

	Distance travelled	Time taken for each lap
Lap 1	10 km	1 hour
Lap 2	10 km	30 minutes
Lap 3	10 km	30 minutes
Lap 4	10 km	2 hours

You can plot the race onto a distance–time graph.

▶ You plot time on the horizontal axis and distance on the vertical axis.

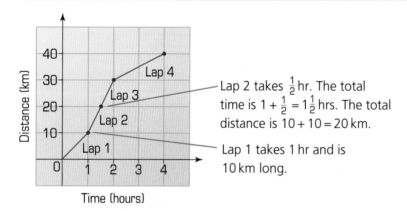

Lap 2 takes $\frac{1}{2}$ hr. The total time is $1 + \frac{1}{2} = 1\frac{1}{2}$ hrs. The total distance is $10 + 10 = 20$ km.

Lap 1 takes 1 hr and is 10 km long.

You can calculate the speed of each lap using the graph.

Lap 1: the cyclist travelled 10 km in 1 hour
        so the speed is 10 km/h.

Lap 2: the cyclist travelled 10 km in 30 minutes
        so the speed is 20 km in 1 hour or 20 km/h.

For the whole route: the cyclist travelled 40 km in 4 hours.

Speed for whole route $= \dfrac{40}{4} = 10$ km/h

▶ Speed $= \dfrac{\text{distance travelled}}{\text{time taken}}$

Exercise A4.9

1 Write the speed shown on each graph for each journey.

a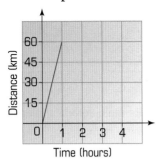

Time (hours)

b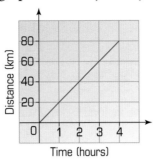

Time (hours)

c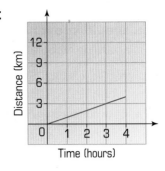

Time (hours)

2 There are 3 stages in this journey.
   a Calculate the speed of each stage.
   b Calculate the speed of the whole journey.

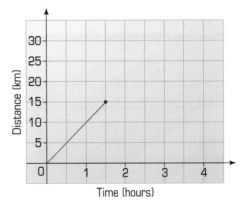

3 The graph shows the first stage of Lucy's journey.
   a How long did the journey take?
   b What was her speed?
   For the second stage of her journey she travels
   for 2 hours at 5 km/h.
   c Copy the graph. Draw the second stage
   of Lucy's journey on your graph.
   d How far does she travel in this stage of her
   journey?
   e How far has she travelled altogether?
   f How long has her total journey taken?

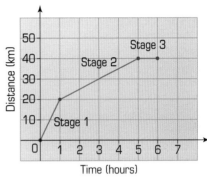

4 On axes like these, draw graphs to represent these journeys.
   a A cyclist pedals at 10 km/h for 1 hour.
   She rests for 1 hour then cycles again for
   2 hours at a speed of 20 km/h.
   b Jimmy rides his scooter for 1 hour at a
   speed of 20 km/h.
   He stops and does his shopping for 1 hour.
   Then he rides at 40 km/h for another
   30 minutes ($\frac{1}{2}$ hour).

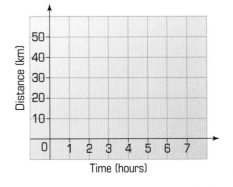

You should know how to …

1 Find common multiples.

2 Factorise numbers up to 100 into prime factors.

3 Find the difference between a positive and a negative number.

4 Plot graphs of simple linear functions.

Check out

1 a Write the first 10 multiples of 4.

  b Write the first 10 multiples of 7.

  c What is the lowest common multiple of 4 and 7?

2 Copy and complete the diagrams to find the prime factors of these numbers.

  a

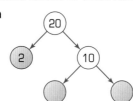

  b

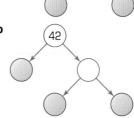

3 Copy and complete these calculations.
You can use the number line to help you.

  a $^-3 + 7 =$ **b** $^-1 + 6 =$

  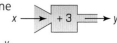

  $$-5 \quad -4 \quad -3 \quad -2 \quad -1 \quad 0 \quad 1 \quad 2 \quad 3 \quad 4 \quad 5$$

4 For the equation $y = x + 3$:

  a Copy this table of values.

x	0	1	2	3	4
y					

  Use this function machine to complete the table.

  $$x \longrightarrow \boxed{+ 3} \Longrightarrow y$$

  b Plot the x- and y-coordinates on a copy of these axes.

  c Check that they make a straight line.

2 Probability

This unit will show you how to:

▶▶ Solve a problem by representing, extracting and interpreting data in tables, graphs and charts.

▶▶ Find the mode and range of a set of data.

▶▶ Use the language associated with probability to discuss events.

▶▶ Find probabilities based on equally likely outcomes.

▶▶ Find probabilities based on experimental data.

The midwife says there's a 50:50 chance it'll be a girl. I'm not sure I believe her!

PRENATAL UNIT

WAY OUT

Some things are unlikely but not impossible!

Before you start

You should know how to ...

1 Use fraction notation.

2 Recognise when 2 simple fractions are equivalent.

Check in

1 What fraction of these rectangles are coloured?

a    b

c 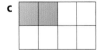   d

2 a Write the fractions in question 1 in their simplest form.

b Which 2 rectangles have the same fraction coloured?

This spread will show you how to:
▶▶ Solve a problem by representing, extracting and interpreting data in tables, graphs and charts.
▶▶ Find the range of a set of data.

KEYWORDS
Range   Class
Interval   Tally
Grouped data

The range of a set of data tells you how spread out the data are.

▶ Range = greatest value – least value.

Here is the weekly pocket money of 5 children:

| £5.00 | £4.25 | £4.00 | £2.50 | £2.00 |

The range is £5.00 – £2.00 = £3.00

To sort a large amount of data you can group the data into classes.

30 students do a Maths test. Here are the results:

26	29	30	31	31
36	38	39	40	40
43	47	47	48	49
50	51	53	53	55
56	57	58	58	58
60	63	66	68	69

You can group the data into classes. Each class covers 10 marks.

Marks	Tally	Frequency
20–29	II	2
30–39	ЖHT I	6
40–49	ЖHT II	7
50–59	ЖHT ЖHT	10
60–69	ЖHT	5

You can show the data on a bar chart.

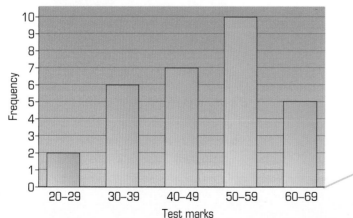

Each group of data is called a class

The size of the class is called the interval.
Intervals should be the same size.
These intervals are 10 marks.

Exercise D2.1

1 Find the range for each of these sets of data:

   a 4, 5, 6, 6, 7, 9, 10, 15   **b** 8, 10, 11, 14, 14, 16, 18, 22

   c 16, 5, 12, 19, 8, 12, 7, 5   **d** 12.5, 6.8, 4, 7.5, 9, 8, 10.3

2 Tom wants to sort his data into classes.

   The size of each interval is 5.

   a Copy and complete the table to show the classes.

0–4	5–9	10–__	__–__	__–24

   b Tom changes the size of each interval to 8.

      Copy and complete the table to show the new classes.

0–7	8–15	16–__	__–__	__–39

3 This list shows the ages of the first 20 people to enter Thorp
Towers Theme Park one Saturday.

8	13	18	7	23	7	11	25	12	15
10	16	15	16	18	9	14	19	13	9

   a Copy and complete the classes in this frequency table.
The size of each interval is 5 years.

Age	Tally	Frequency
6–		
–		
–		
–		

   b Tally the list of ages on your copy of the frequency table and
write in the frequency.

   c Copy and complete this bar chart using the information from
the frequency table.

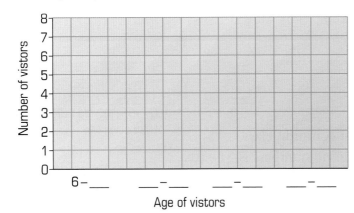

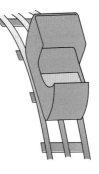

This spread will show you how to:

▸▸ Solve a problem by representing, extracting and interpreting data in tables, graphs and charts.
▸▸ Find the mode of a set of data.

KEYWORDS

Class   Modal class
Interval

At Compton High School, Year 9 students are given Merits for effort and excellent work.
Reena wants to know:

▸ The most common number of Merits (the **mode**)
▸ How many students got a Gold Prize for 100 Merits or more.

▸ Mode = the most common value.

She sorts her data into classes to make it easier to understand.
She looks for the modal class.

example

The winning numbers in a weekly raffle are recorded for 30 weeks.

86	224	61	106	34	173	207	239	63	14
162	78	185	50	137	23	15	36	188	71
130	97	114	236	239	6	149	224	55	22

a Sort this data using a frequency table. The size of the class intervals is 50.
b Display this data on a bar chart.
c What is the modal class?

....

a Work out the class intervals and tally in the numbers.

Numbers	Tally	Frequency
1–50	卌 I	6
51–100	卌 III	8
101–150	卌	5
151–200	IIII	4
201–250	卌 II	7

b Use the same class intervals to record the data onto a bar chart.

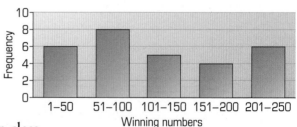

c The modal class is the most common class.
The modal class of the winning numbers is 51–100.

Exercise D2.2

1 Here is a record of the number of Merits awarded to 80 Year 9 students.

```
  9  12  12  15  17  18  19  23  25  27
 27  27  28  30  32  33  33  35  36  37
 37  37  39  42  46  49  51  53  57  58
 59  59  62  66  67  67  68  70  71  71
 73  74  74  75  76  76  77  78  78  79
 79  79  81  83  84  88  90  90  91  92
 93  93  93  94  94  95  96  96  98 100
103 104 109 110 112 114 117 121 124 127
```

a What is the range of this data?

b Decide on a good size of class interval to group the data.

c Draw a frequency table to tally the results.
This one is started for you:

Number of Merits	Tally	Frequency

d Draw a bar chart to show this data.
Give it the title 'Year 9 Merits'.

2 **a** What is the modal class of the data in question 1?

b What fraction of these students receive a Gold Prize
(100 Merits or more)?

3 A scientist divided a forest into 80 equal areas.
Here is a record of the number of trees in each area.

```
55  29  43  93  56  29  67  41  33  96
26  48   3  72  27  53  22   9  85  56
79  91  65  42  89  47  79  73  34  45
10  47  27  54  66   8  42  58  17  37
58  73  23  36  41  62  32  83  57  43
62  17  54  77  32  34  48  23  40  49
49  58  25  16  51  61  60  69  48  27
37  72  58  62  42  56   5  45  35  63
```

a Sort this data into classes using a frequency table.

b Display the data on a bar chart.

c What is the modal class?

> You need to decide your class interval first.

This spread will show you how to:

▶▶ Use the language associated with probability to discuss events.

▶ The probability of an event can be described in words.

It is not certain that buses will keep arriving at a bus stop but it is very likely.

It is not impossible for it to snow in July or August in Europe, but it is very unlikely.

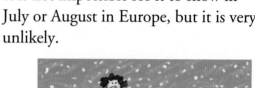

The probability of picking a black card from these cards is certain, because they are all black cards.

The probability of choosing a red card is impossible, because there are no red cards.

You can write this on a probability scale from 0 to 1:

Impossible   Even chance   Certain

0   1

The probability of picking a red card is 0.   The probability of picking a black card is 1.

▶ You can also use fractions to describe probabilities.

It is not certain that you would pick a red card at random from these cards, but it is very likely.

It is not impossible to pick a black card but it is unlikely.

The probability of picking a red card is 4 chances in 5 $= \frac{4}{5}$.

The probability of picking a black card is 1 chance in 5 $= \frac{1}{5}$.

Exercise D2.3

1 Pick a word from the ring to describe each of the events in the boxes.

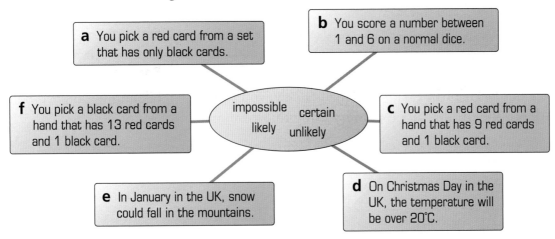

a You pick a red card from a set that has only black cards.

b You score a number between 1 and 6 on a normal dice.

f You pick a black card from a hand that has 13 red cards and 1 black card.

impossible certain
likely unlikely

c You pick a red card from a hand that has 9 red cards and 1 black card.

e In January in the UK, snow could fall in the mountains.

d On Christmas Day in the UK, the temperature will be over 20°C.

2 Match each bag with 1 of the statements.
Use the bag to copy and complete the statements.

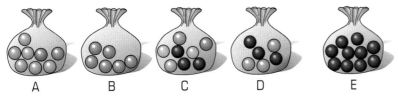

A   B   C   D   E

a It is unlikely that you can pick a red bead from bag ____
b It is certain that you would pick a black bead from bag ____
c It is likely that you would pick a _____ bead from bag ____
d It is equally likely that you would pick a red or black bead from bag ____

3 Here are 4 sets of cards.

A   B   C   D

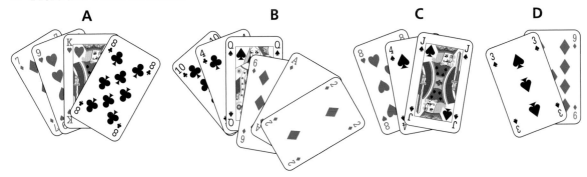

a Which set shows a probability of $\frac{3}{4}$ for picking a red card?
b Which set shows a probability of $\frac{2}{3}$ for picking a black card?
c In which 2 sets is there an equal chance of picking a red or black card?
d What is the chance of picking a black card from set B?

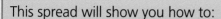
This spread will show you how to:
▶▶ Find the probabilities based on equally likely outcomes.
▶▶ Find probabilities based on experimental data.

KEYWORDS

Outcome   Event
Experiment   Trial
Theoretical probability
Experimental probability

If the outcomes of an event are equally likely, you can work out the theoretical probability using this formula:

▶ Probability of an event = $\dfrac{\text{number of favourable outcomes}}{\text{total number of outcomes}}$

The favourable outcomes are the results you are looking for.

example

Barney rolls a fair dice.
What is the probability he will roll an odd number?

There are 6 possible outcomes: 1, 2, 3, 4, 5 or 6
There are 3 favourable outcomes: 1, 3 or 5.

Theoretical probability of an event = $\dfrac{\text{number of favourable outcomes}}{\text{number of outcomes}} = \dfrac{3}{6}$

The probability of Barney rolling an odd number is $\dfrac{3}{6} = \dfrac{1}{2}$.

If you don't know that the outcomes are all equally likely, you can estimate the probability using an experiment.

▶ Experimental probability of an event = $\dfrac{\text{number of successful trials}}{\text{total number of trials}}$

An experiment is a series of trials.

example

Ruby is shooting a basketball at a hoop.
She takes 20 shots. She makes 5 baskets.
What is the probability she will score a basket each time she shoots?

The whole experiment was 20 shots.
Each shot was a trial.

Experimental probability = $\dfrac{\text{number of successful trials}}{\text{number of trials}} = \dfrac{5}{20}$

The probability of Ruby scoring with each shot is $\dfrac{5}{20} = \dfrac{1}{4}$.

Exercise D2.4

1 Sarah picks one of these cards without looking:

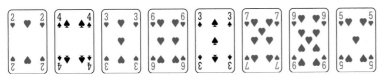

a She says: 'I'm more likely to pick a black card than a red card.'
Explain why she is wrong.

b Find the probability that she picks:

   i   an even number
   ii an odd number
   iii a black card
   iv a number 4
   v   a number less than 9.

2 Toby picks a marble from one of these jars without looking:

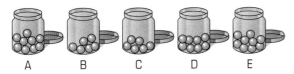

Write which jar he picks from if:

a It is certain he will pick blue.

b It is impossible for him to pick blue.

c There is an even chance he will pick red.

d It is unlikely he will pick blue.

e The probability of picking red is $\frac{1}{3}$.

3 Sam records the weather outside her window for 20 days.
Here are her results:

	Tally	Frequency
Dry	⊬⊬ ⊬⊬ ⊬⊬	15
Wet	⊬⊬	5

Use the data to find the probability of it raining the next day.

4 Gemma is practising taking penalties.
She takes 20 shots at the goal.
Here are her results:

Saved	Miss	Saved	Goal	Saved	Goal	Miss
Goal	Saved	Saved	Saved	Miss	Goal	Goal
Goal	Goal	Saved	Miss	Saved	Saved	

Use the data to find the probability of her next shot being:

a saved   **b** a miss   **c** a goal.

Write your answers as fractions.

You should know how to ...

1 Solve a problem by representing, extracting and interpreting data in tables, graphs and charts.

2 Find the mode and range of a set of data.
- ▶ Mode = most common value
- ▶ Range = greatest value – least value

3 Use the language associated with probability to discuss events.

Check out

1 Here are the number of people in 40 households in a street.

3	4	1	2	5	4	2	4	3	2
4	2	3	4	4	3	4	5	1	3
4	4	5	3	1	2	3	4	4	3
6	4	3	4	4	5	3	1	2	4

  a Make a tally chart to sort this data.
  b Draw a bar chart to show the data.
  c In how many households are there 2 people?

2 a Find the mode of the data in question 1.
  b Find the range of the data in question 1.

3 Jane is doing a survey in the street in question 1.
  a Copy and complete these statements.
   i It is ___ Jane will find a household with 10 people.
   ii It is ___ she will find a household with fewer than 7 people.
  b What is the probability she will find a household with 3 people?

3 Transformations

This unit will show you how to:

- ▶▶ Use a protractor to measure angles to the nearest degree.
- ▶▶ Recognise where a shape will be after a reflection, translation or rotation.
- ▶▶ Recognise where a shape will be after a reflection in 2 mirror lines at right angles.
- ▶▶ Recognise where a shape will be after 2 translations.

- ▶▶ Identify all the symmetries of 2-D shapes.
- ▶▶ Recognise and explain patterns and relationships.
- ▶▶ Enlarge 2-D shapes.
- ▶▶ Solve simple problems involving ratio and proportion.
- ▶▶ Use, read and write standard metric units.
- ▶▶ Convert between units and measures.

Flowers can be symmetrical or have no symmetry.

Before you start

You should know how to ...

1 Recognise quarter turns.

Check in

1 **a** Which of these angles is a quarter turn?

    i   ii   iii

  b How many quarter turns are there in a full turn?

2 Know multiples up to 10 × 10.

2 **a** What are the first 5 multiples of 2?

  b What are the first 5 multiples of 3?

This spread will show you how to:

▶▶ Use a protractor to measure angles to the nearest degree.

KEYWORDS

Bearing   Protractor
Clockwise   Compass

Rachel is standing at the top of a tower.
She is looking North.
She turns clockwise through an angle of 60° and can see Shepherd's Hill.

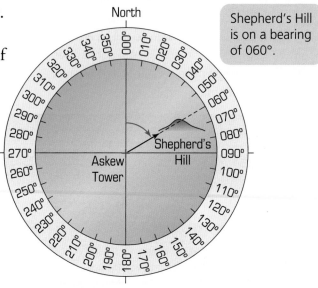

Shepherd's Hill is on a bearing of 060°.

▶ The angle of turn from North is called a bearing.

To give an accurate bearing:

▶ Use the 360° scale.
▶ Measure from North.
▶ Measure clockwise.
▶ Use 3 figures.

You can measure any bearing up to 180° directly with a protractor.

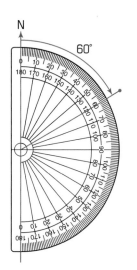

For a bearing greater than 180° you can still use a protractor.

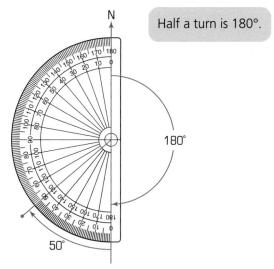

Half a turn is 180°.

Use the protractor to measure the rest of the angle past 180°.
Add this to 180° to measure the whole bearing. 180° + 50° = 230°

Exercise S3.1

1 Ryan is standing beside the lake.

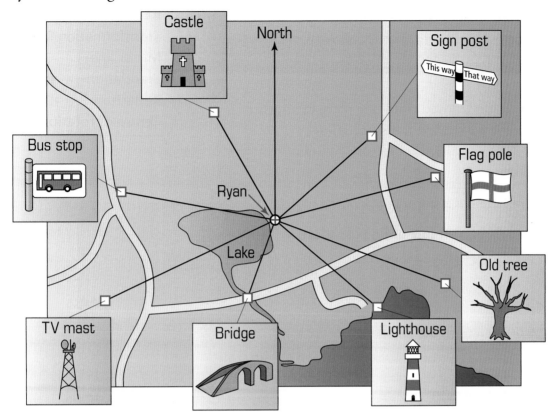

What will Ryan see on a bearing of:
a 130°   **b** 075°   **c** 200°   **d** 330°

2 Give a bearing for each of these points from Ryan.
   a The old tree   **b** The bus stop
   c The TV mast   **d** The sign post

3 Use this compass to answer these questions.
   What would Ryan see if he looked to the:
   a south-east?
   b north-east?
   c south-west?

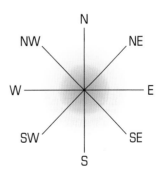

4 a Copy the compass accurately.
   b Use your compass to copy and complete the table.

Direction	N					SW	W	NW
Bearing	000°	045°	090°	135°	180°			

This spread will show you how to:

▶▶ Recognise where a shape will be after a reflection, translation or rotation.

KEYWORDS

Transformation   Rotation
Mirror line   Object
Translation   Image
Reflection   Direction
Centre of rotation

A shape can be moved from one place to another in different ways called transformations.

Reflection

▶ A reflection is a mirror image of the object.

You give the mirror line or line of reflection.

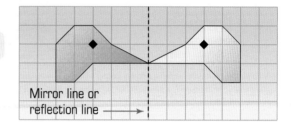

Mirror line or reflection line ⟶

Rotation

▶ A rotation turns the object.

You give:

▶ The angle of turn
▶ The centre of rotation
  – the point about which it turns.
▶ The direction of turn
  – clockwise or anticlockwise.

90°
rotation
anticlockwise

Centre of rotation

Translation

▶ A translation slides the object.

You give:

▶ the distance moved left or right, then
▶ the distance moved up or down.

The translation 6 to the left, and 4 down can be written:

$$\begin{pmatrix} 6 \text{ left} \\ 4 \text{ down} \end{pmatrix}$$

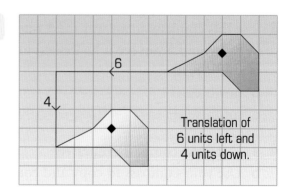

6

4

Translation of 6 units left and 4 units down.

Exercise S3.2

1 a Copy each shape onto squared paper.
  b Reflect each shape in the mirror line.
  c Name the new shape you have made.
  d Mark the equal angles and equal sides on the new shape.

 i    ii   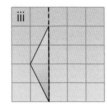 iii   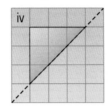 iv   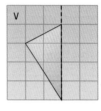 v

2 The centre of rotation for each of these shapes is shown by a red dot.
  Copy each shape onto squared paper and rotate each shape through 90° clockwise.

 a   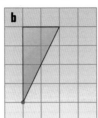 b   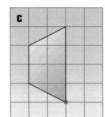 c    d   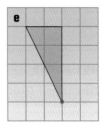 e

3 Copy the grid and shape. Translate the shape following each of these instructions. Start from the original shape each time.

a $\begin{pmatrix} 5 \text{ left} \\ 7 \text{ down} \end{pmatrix}$

b $\begin{pmatrix} 3 \text{ right} \\ 6 \text{ up} \end{pmatrix}$

c $\begin{pmatrix} 0 \text{ left} \\ 6 \text{ down} \end{pmatrix}$

d $\begin{pmatrix} 7 \text{ left} \\ 4 \text{ up} \end{pmatrix}$

e $\begin{pmatrix} 6 \text{ right} \\ 4 \text{ down} \end{pmatrix}$

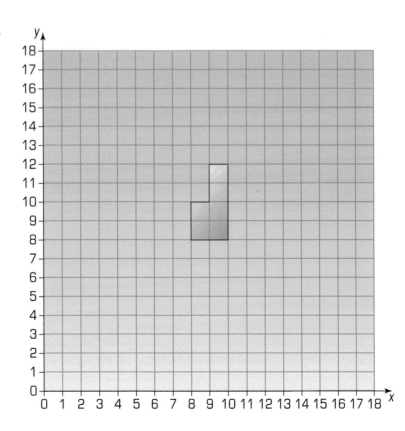

This spread will show you how to:

▶▶ Recognise where a shape will be after a reflection or translation.

▶▶ Recognise where a shape will be after 2 translations.

KEYWORDS

Reflection   Rotation

Image   Object

Translation

Reflection

When you reflect an object in a diagonal mirror line you must make sure that:

▶ equivalent points on the object and the image are the same distance from the mirror line.

AO = OB

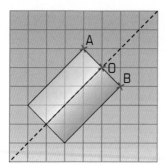

You can turn the page so that the line is horizontal to help you.

Translations

You can do more than 1 translation.

example

Translate this shape by:

▶ 4 right, then by

▶ 2 left and 4 down.

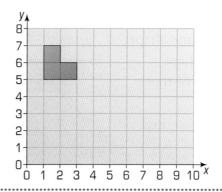

Do the first translation:

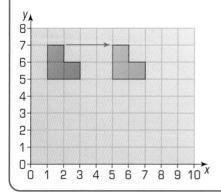

then the second:

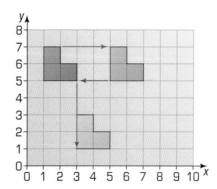

Exercise S3.3

1 a Copy this grid.
Draw a diagonal mirror line from
corner to corner.
Draw triangle ABC.

b Draw the reflection of points A,
B and C and label them D, E and F.

c Give the coordinates of points D,
E and F.

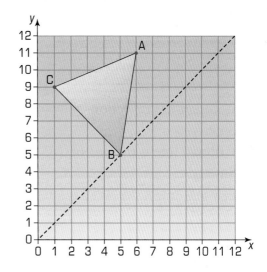

2 Copy the grid and shape.
Translate the shape following each
of these instructions.
Start from the original shape each
time.

a $\begin{pmatrix} 6 \text{ right} \\ 4 \text{ down} \end{pmatrix}$ then $\begin{pmatrix} 5 \text{ left} \\ 0 \text{ down} \end{pmatrix}$

b $\begin{pmatrix} 3 \text{ right} \\ 2 \text{ up} \end{pmatrix}$ then $\begin{pmatrix} 0 \text{ right} \\ 5 \text{ down} \end{pmatrix}$

c $\begin{pmatrix} 5 \text{ right} \\ 4 \text{ down} \end{pmatrix}$ then $\begin{pmatrix} 4 \text{ left} \\ 2 \text{ up} \end{pmatrix}$

d $\begin{pmatrix} 6 \text{ left} \\ 3 \text{ up} \end{pmatrix}$ then $\begin{pmatrix} 2 \text{ left} \\ 2 \text{ up} \end{pmatrix}$

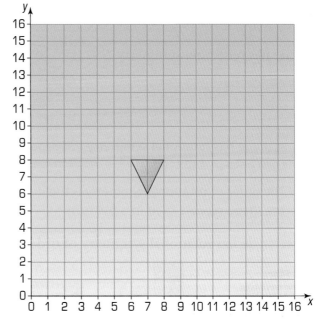

3 You can also do more than one reflection.
Copy this grid and shapes A and B.
Reflect these shapes in Line 1, then reflect the
new image in Line 2.
The first one has been done for you.

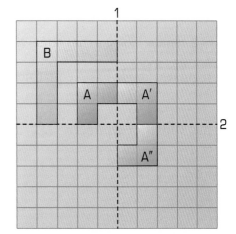

This spread will show you how to:

▶▶ Identify all the symmetries of 2-D shapes.

KEYWORDS
Reflection symmetry
Line of symmetry
Order of rotational
   symmetry

This design has reflection symmetry.
The dotted line is the line of symmetry.

> ▶ A shape has **reflection symmetry** if you can fold it so that one half fits exactly on top of the other.

A kite has reflection symmetry.

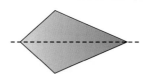

> ▶ A shape has **rotational symmetry** if it repeats itself more than once in a full turn.
>
> ▶ The order of rotational symmetry is the number of times the shape repeats itself in a full turn.

A rectangle has rotational symmetry of order 2:

Start

 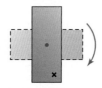 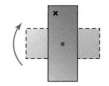

> ▶ A regular polygon has equal sides and equal angles.

A regular triangle has 3 equal sides and 3 equal angles.

It is called an equilateral triangle

It has 3 lines of symmetry ...   and rotational symmetry of order 3.

Exercise S3.4

1 Copy and complete this table.
Draw each shape and mark all the lines of symmetry.
Write the order of rotational symmetry.

	Shape	Lines of symmetry	Order of rotational symmetry
a	square		4
b	rectangle		
c	parallelogram		
d	rhombus		
e	kite		
f	delta (arrowhead)		
g	equilateral triangle		
h	isosceles triangle		

2 Copy this grid.
  a Reflect the kite in the *x*-axis
  b Reflect the kite in the *y*-axis.
  c Complete the pattern to make a star.
  d How may lines of symmetry does the star have?
  e What is the order of rotational symmetry of the star?

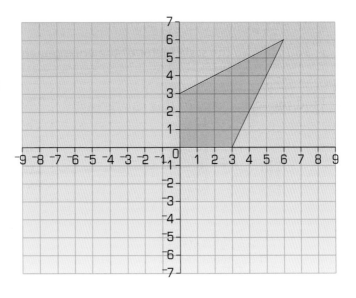

This spread will show you how to:

▶▶ Enlarge 2-D shapes.
▶▶ Solve simple problems involving ratio and proportion.

KEYWORDS
Enlargement   Ratio
Scale factor

This photograph has been made bigger ... it has been enlarged.

2 × larger

All the lengths have been multiplied by 2.
This is an enlargement, scale factor 2.

You can show an enlargement on a grid.

example

Enlarge this shape by a factor of 3.

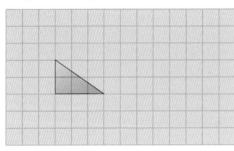

All the lengths must be 3 times longer:

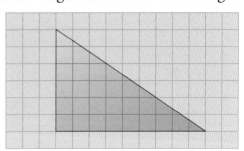

▶ An enlargement changes all the measurements of a shape in the same proportion.

▶ You can give the scale factor of the enlargement.

example

Find the scale factor of this enlargement.

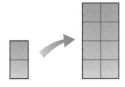

The lengths are in the same ratio.

The original height was 2.
The new height is 4.
The original width was 1.
The new width is 2.
The scale factor is 2.

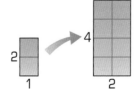

Exercise S3.5

1 Copy each shape onto squared paper.
Enlarge each shape by scale factor 2.

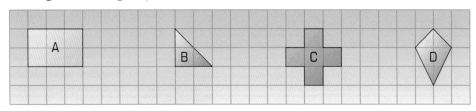

2 Find the scale factor for these enlargements.

a

b

c

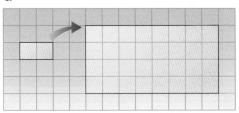
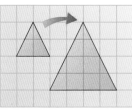
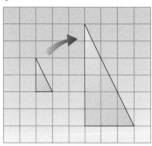

3 Draw a rectangle 3 cm wide and 2 cm high on squared paper.
Draw an enlargement of this rectangle with scale factor 3.
Label it: Enlargement scale factor 3.

4 a Copy this grid and the star shape.
The coordinates for the star shape are:

A (5, 8)   B (6, 6)   C (8, 5)
D (6, 4)   E (5, 2)   F (4, 4)
G (2, 5)   H (4, 6)

b Multiply each co-ordinate pair by 2;
so A (5, 8) ⟶ A′ (10, 16)

c Plot each new point onto your grid.

d What is the scale factor of this enlargement?

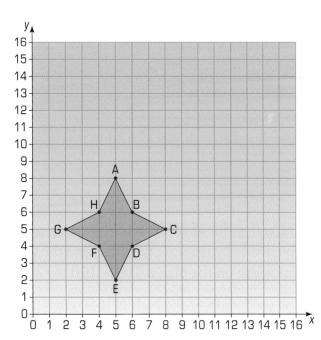

This spread will show you how to:
▶▶ Use, read and write standard metric units.
▶▶ Solve simple problems involving ratio and proportion.

KEYWORDS
Scale drawing   Ratio
Scale

Here is a door knob for a bathroom cupboard.
It is shown life-size.
The door is too big to fit onto the page,
so you need a scale drawing.

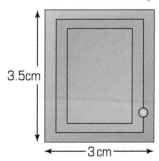

The scale of the drawing is: 1 cm represents 10 cm
You can write the ratio as 1 cm : 10 cm or 1 : 10

example

What are the real height and width of this door?

The scale drawing of the door is 3 cm wide.

The real door will be 10 times wider = 30 cm.

The scale drawing is 3.5 cm tall, so the real door will be 35 cm tall.

example

Here is a sketch showing the dimensions of a bath.
How wide and how long would the bath be on a
plan drawn to a scale of 1 : 100?

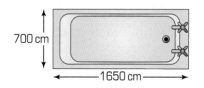

The real width of the bath is 700 cm.
You divide by the scale factor to find the width on the plan.
The width on the plan is 700 ÷ 100 = 7 cm.

The real length of the bath is 1650 cm.
The length on the plan is 1650 ÷ 100 = 16.5 cm.

Exercise S3.6

1 Here are 3 picture frames.
They are drawn to scale – 1 cm : 10 cm (1 : 10).
Measure each frame and calculate its actual length and width.

Frame A

Frame B

Frame C

2 Here is a plan of a children's play area.
It is drawn to a scale of 1 cm : 1 m (1 : 100).

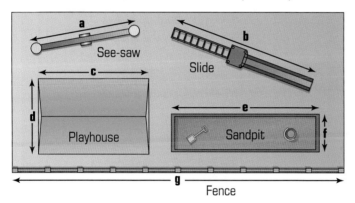

Work out:
a The length of the see-saw.
b The length of the slide.
c The length of the playhouse.
d The width of the playhouse.
e The length of the sand pit.
f The width of the sand pit.
g The length of the fence.

3 Rory the builder makes a rough sketch of a room.
Re-draw his sketch to the correct scale.
Use a scale of 2 cm to represent 1 m (1 : 50).

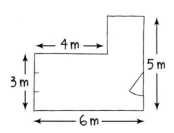

You should know how to ...

1 Use a protractor to measure angles to the nearest degree.

2 Recognise where a shape will be after a reflection, translation or rotation.

3 Solve simple problems involving ratio and proportion.

Check out

1 Use a protractor to measure these angles.

a

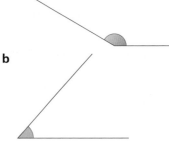

b

2 a The green triangle is reflected in the *y*-axis.
What colour is the image?

b The green triangle is rotated a quarter turn clockwise about point A.
What colour is the image?

c The green triangle is translated 3 left and 2 down.
What colour is the image?

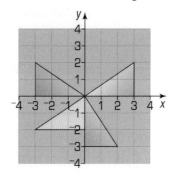

3 Find the scale factor of this enlargement.

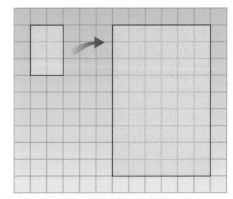

This unit will show you how to:

- ▶▶ Use the language associated with probability to discuss events.
- ▶▶ Find the mode, range, median and mean of a set of data.
- ▶▶ Solve a problem by extracting and interpreting data in tables, graphs and charts.
- ▶▶ Represent problems mathematically.

- ▶▶ Choose and use appropriate strategies to solve number problems.
- ▶▶ Calculate the perimeter and area of shapes.
- ▶▶ Use standard measures.
- ▶▶ Use knowledge and skills from different mathematical areas to solve problems.
- ▶▶ Check results using appropriate methods.

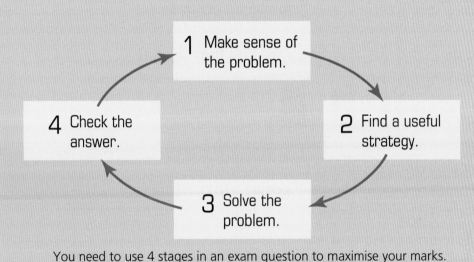

1 Make sense of the problem.

2 Find a useful strategy.

3 Solve the problem.

4 Check the answer.

You need to use 4 stages in an exam question to maximise your marks.

Before you start

You should know how to ...

- ▶ Use probabilities.
- ▶ Find and use the mode, median, mean and range.
- ▶ Interpret graphs and diagrams.
- ▶ Use letter symbols.
- ▶ Solve simple equations.
- ▶ Round numbers.
- ▶ Add, subtract, multiply and divide integers and decimals.

- ▶ Use the equivalence of fractions, decimals and percentages.
- ▶ Use units of measurement.
- ▶ Know and use formulas for perimeter and area.
- ▶ Use the order of operations.
- ▶ Solve problems using ideas of ratio and proportion.

This spread will show you how to:
- ▶▶ Use the language associated with probability.
- ▶▶ Find the mode, range, median and mean.

KEYWORDS
Probability   Median
Mean   Range
Mode

Before you answer a question you need to work out:
- ▶ what the question is about
- ▶ what it is asking you to find out
- ▶ what information it gives to help you.

- ▶ The probability of an event = $\dfrac{\text{number of favourable outcomes}}{\text{total number of outcomes}}$.

example

What is the probability of picking a red card from this set?

This is a probability question.
You are working out the chance of getting a red card.

There are 4 red cards. There are 5 cards in total.

The probability of a red card = $\frac{4}{5}$.

Write the facts you know.

- ▶ The mode is the most common value.
- ▶ The median is the middle value when the data are in order.
- ▶ The mean is the total of the values divided by the number of values.
- ▶ The range is the difference between the largest and smallest values.

example

Here are 10 numbers: 3, 4, 5, 5, 5, 5, 7, 8, 9, 9

Find: **a** the mode   **b** the range   **c** the median   **d** the mean.

a The mode is 5, as it occurs most often (4 times).
b The range is $9 - 3 = 6$.
c The median value is 5. 3, 4, 5, 5, 5, 5, 7, 8, 9, 9
d The mean = $\frac{60}{10} = 6$.

Many questions ask you to explain your answer or show your working out.
Make sure you write out all your steps!

Exercise P1.1

1 a Clio has 4 coins.

She picks one of these coins at random.
As a fraction, what is the probability that she gets a 10p piece?

b Ryan has 4 coins that total 18p.
He picks one of his coins at random.
What is the probability that he gets a 10p coin?
You must show your working.

2 a Carl has these cards:
Linda takes a card without looking.
Carl says:

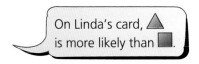

Explain why Carl is wrong.

b Here are some words and phrases

Choose a word or phrase to fill in the gaps below.

i It is _____ that the number on Linda's card will be smaller than 10.

ii It is _____ that the number on Linda's card will be an odd number.

3 Sarah rolls a dice 10 times.
Here are the scores:
What is the modal score?

2 5 4 5 1 6 6 3 2 5

4 There are 4 people in Ashraf's family.
Their shoe sizes are 3, 4, 6 and 9.
What is the median shoe size in Ashraf's family?

5 The mean of these numbers is 5.
Write 3 numbers that have a mean of 6.

KEYWORDS

Scale

Key

Grouped data

This spread will show you how to:

▶▶ Solve a problem by extracting and interpreting data in tables, graphs and charts.

You often need to find information from tables, graphs and charts.

You need to look at:

▶ the type of graph or chart
▶ the scale
▶ the key.

example

This table shows how much it costs to go from Oxford to London on the train.

Jon wants to take his son (aged 10) and father (aged 67) to London for a day out.

How much will he save if they wait until after 9 am?

	Before 9 am	After 9 am
Adult	£35.00	£27.50
Child (14 or under)	£21.80	£16.50
Senior (65 or over)	£23.50	£21.70

You need to find the total cost before and after 9 am.

Before 9 am:
```
  35.00
  21.80
  23.50 +
  80.30     It costs £80.30 before 9 am.
```

After 9 am:
```
  27.50
  16.50
  21.70 +
  65.70     It costs £65.70 after 9 am.
```

£80.30 − £65.70

0.6 + 4 + 10 = 14.6

So Jon saves £14.60 by waiting until after 9 am.

Many questions ask you to explain your answer.

Make sure you write out all your steps!

Exercise P1.2

1 Jamie visited a safari park.
The pictogram shows how many animals he saw.
  a How many lions did Jamie see?
  b Jamie saw more zebras than elephants.
  How many more?

Key: ● represents 10 animals

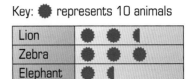

Lion	● ● ◖
Zebra	● ● ●
Elephant	● ◖

2 The table shows distances between some towns.

Distances in miles

	Hereford	Norwich	Plymouth	York
Hereford				
Norwich	215			
Plymouth	169	364		
York	192	180	339	

  a Which two towns are the shortest distance apart?
  b Mrs Prior drove from Plymouth to Norwich.
  What is the distance between Plymouth and Norwich?

  c Then Mrs Prior drove from Norwich to York.
  What is the distance between Norwich and York?

  d How far did Mrs Prior drive altogether?

> You need to interpret your answer.

3 The bar charts show how many students went to a Maths club.

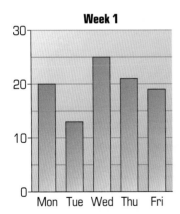

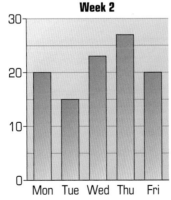

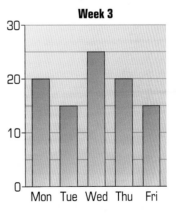

Here are 3 statements.
  a In each week, the day with the most students was Wednesday.
  b In each week, the same number of students went to the club on Monday.
  c In each week, the same students went to the club on Monday.

Use the graphs to decide if each statement is:
    True   False   Not enough information
Explain your answer.

Solving algebra problems

This spread will show you how to:

▶▶ Represent problems mathematically.

KEYWORDS
Balance   Equals

An equals sign (=) shows that 2 quantities are exactly the same.
They balance.

2 cans balance with 1 box

2 boxes balance with 1 bottle

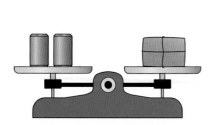

2 cans = 1 box

2 boxes = 1 bottle

You can use these relationships to solve problems.

example

a How many cans will balance with 1 bottle?

b How many cans will balance with 1 bottle and 1 box together?

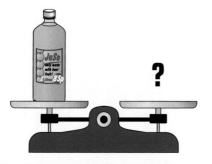

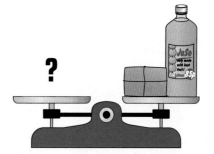

a Read the question carefully.

$$1 \text{ bottle} \rightarrow 2 \text{ boxes}$$
$$1 \text{ box} \rightarrow 2 \text{ cans}$$

So you need 4 cans to balance with 1 bottle.

b 4 cans balance with 1 bottle and 2 cans balance with 1 box.

$$4 + 2 = 6$$

You need 6 cans to balance with 1 bottle and 1 box together.

Exercise P1.3

Richard balances 3 cans with 1 box.   He balances 3 boxes with 1 bottle.

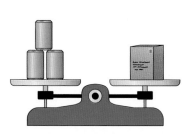
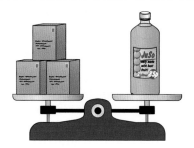

1 How many cans does Richard need to balance 2 boxes?

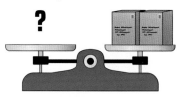

2 How many bottles does he need to balance 6 boxes?

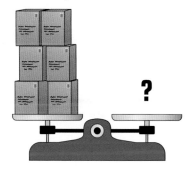

3 How many cans does he need to balance 1 bottle?

4 Draw scales like these. Show how you could make these items balance on the scales.

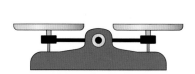

This spread will show you how to:
- ▶▶ Choose and use appropriate strategies to solve number problems.
- ▶▶ Construct and solve simple linear equations.
- ▶▶ Record readings from scales.

KEYWORDS

Jottings

There are 2 small parcels and 1 large parcel on these scales.

The small parcels have the same weight.
The weight of the large parcel is 3.2 kg.

There are 2 ways to find the weight of a small parcel.

Method 1: Using jottings

Subtract the weight of the large parcel from the total:
$8 - 3.2 = 4.8$

The 2 small parcels weigh 4.8 kg altogether.

Divide by 2: $4.8 \div 2 = 2.4$

Each small parcel weighs 2.4 kg.

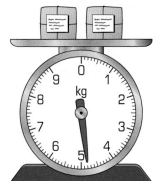

Method 2: Using algebra

Use W to stand for the weight of each small parcel.

$$2 \times W + 3.2 = 8 \text{ kg}$$

$W \longrightarrow \boxed{\times 2} \Longrightarrow \boxed{+3.2} \Longrightarrow 8$

$2.4 \longleftarrow \boxed{\div 2} \longleftarrow \boxed{-3.2} \longleftarrow 8$

The weight of each small parcel is 2.4 kg.

Whichever method you choose, always check your answer.

The total of all the parcels $= 2.4 + 2.4 + 3.2 = 8$ kg.

Exercise P1.4

1 The weight of the large parcel is 1.6 kg.
The small parcels are both the same weight.
Calculate the weight of each small parcel.

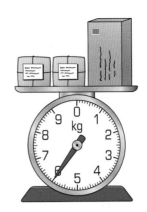

2 Each of the small parcels weighs the same.
The large parcel weighs 2.7 kg.
Calculate the weight of each small parcel.

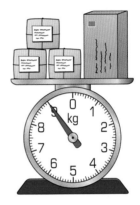

3 These parcels have the same weight.
  a Calculate the weight of 1 parcel.
  b How many parcels will there be on the scales
    when the scales read 6 kg?
  c The scales can weigh up to 10 kg.
    How many parcels will the scales take?

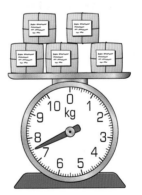

4 The small parcels are half the weight of the large
parcel.
Altogether the parcels weigh 10 kg.
Calculate the weight of each parcel.

Solving measure problems

This spread will show you how to:

⯈⯈ Calculate the perimeter and area of shapes.

⯈⯈ Use standard measures.

You will need to know how to work out the perimeter and area of different shapes.

▶ Perimeter = distance around a shape.

▶ Area = space covered by a shape.
Area is measured in squares.

Exam questions include a space for your answer. The **units** may be given here as a clue.

▶ The area of a rectangle = length × width.
▶ The area of a triangle = $\frac{1}{2}$ × area of enclosing rectangle.

---

example

Find the area and perimeter of these shapes.

a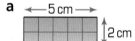

b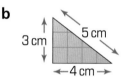

You can also find the area by counting squares.

....

a Perimeter = 5 + 2 + 5 + 2 = 14 cm.
Area = 5 × 2 = 10 cm²

b Perimeter = 5 + 3 + 4 = 12 cm
Area = $\frac{1}{2}$ × 4 × 3 = 6 cm²

You can split up some shapes into rectangles to find their area.

example

What is the area of this shape?

....

Split the shape into 2 rectangles.

Area of A = 4 × 3
= 12 cm²

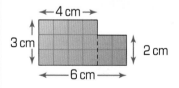

Area of B = 2 × 2
= 4 cm²

Total area = 12 + 4 = 16 cm²

Exercise P1.5

1 The diagram shows some shapes on a 10 by 6 grid.

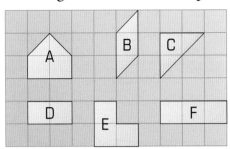

> You can find these areas by counting squares.

  a Which 2 shapes have the same area as shape A?

  b Which 2 shapes have the same perimeter as shape A?

  c How many of shape D would you need to cover a
     10 by 6 square grid?

  d List the shapes that are quadrilaterals.

2 a This triangle is accurately drawn.
    One side is 9.5 cm.

    Tom says:

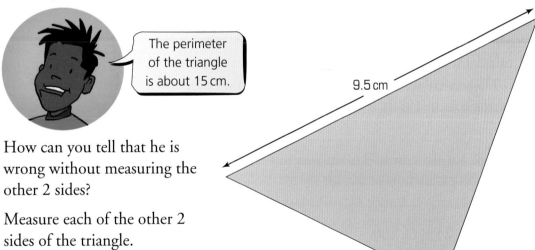

> The perimeter of the triangle is about 15 cm.

9.5 cm

    How can you tell that he is
    wrong without measuring the
    other 2 sides?

  b Measure each of the other 2
    sides of the triangle.
    Write their lengths to the
    nearest 0.1 of a centimetre.

  c Add the lengths of the 3 sides
    of the triangle to find the
    perimeter of the triangle.

> Remember to write down enough working
> to show you have not used a calculator

This spread will show you how to:

▶▶ Use knowledge and skills from different mathematical areas to solve problems.

KEYWORDS
Probability Jottings
Estimate   Grid
Partition

You can simplify fractions by cancelling.

example

Show that the probability of choosing a 50p coin from these coins is $\frac{1}{2}$.

There are 4 coins and 2 of them are 50p coins.
The probability of choosing a 50p = $\frac{2}{4}$.

$$\frac{2}{4} \xrightarrow[\div 2]{\div 2} \frac{1}{2}$$

So the probability of choosing a 50p coin is $\frac{1}{2}$.

You need to be able to work out problems on paper.

example

A calculator costs £1.25.
In 1978 a calculator cost 23 times more than it costs now.
Find the cost in 1978.

To work out the cost of a calculator in 1978 you must multiply £1.25 by 23.
You can use a jottings or a grid.

Jottings

$10 \times £1.25 = £12.50$
so, $20 \times £1.25 = £25.00$
$3 \times £1.00 = £3.00$ and
$3 \times 25p = 75p$

So, the total $= £25 + £3 + 75p$
$= £28.75$

The calculator would have cost £28.75.

Grid

Estimate the answer: £1.25 × 20 = £25
Partition £1.25 into: 100 + 20 + 5 and partition 23 into 20 + 3.

×	100	20	5		
20	2000	400	100	→	2500
3	300	60	15	→ +	375
					2875

Use your estimate to put the decimal point in the correct place.
The estimate is £25 so the answer is £28.75.

Exercise P1.6

1 a What is the probability of picking a 2p coin from these coins?

b Show that the probability of picking a 50p coin is $\frac{1}{2}$.
You must show your working

c Show that the probability of picking a 20p coin is $\frac{1}{3}$.
You must show your working

d Copy and shade $\frac{2}{3}$ of these discs.

2 A calculator costs £1.25.

a In 1995 a calculator would have cost 10 times more
than it would cost now.
Work out the cost of a calculator in 1995.

b In 1989 a calculator would have cost 15 times more
than it would cost now.
Work out the cost of a calculator in 1989.

c Work out the cost of 10 calculators at 1989 prices.

d Scientific calculators cost £6.20.
Work out the cost of 13 scientific calculators.

3 Peter wants to use 5 planks of wood to make a fence.
Each plank of wood is 19 cm wide.
He wants the fence to be 105 cm long with equal spaces between the planks.

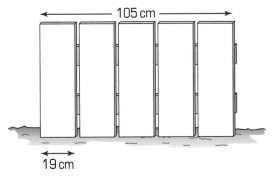

How much space should he leave between each of the planks?
You must show your working.

Summary

You should know how to ...

1 Identify the necessary information to solve a problem.

2 Represent problems and interpret solutions.

Check out

1 a Jenny and her mother each had a set meal at the café.

Café

Set meal

£6.20

Jenny paid with 2 £10 notes.
How much change did she get?

b A party of 12 people each had the set meal. What was the total amount to be paid?

2 Jon has 2 spinners.
He spins them both and adds the scores.

a Copy and complete this table of possible scores.

		Spinner 1		
		1	2	3
Spinner 2	1	2	3	4
	2	3		
	3			

b What is the probability that his score is:
i an even number
ii less than 5?

This unit will show you how to:

▶▶ Use brackets.

▶▶ Develop from explaining a relationship in words to expressing it in a formula using symbols.

▶▶ Substitute positive integers into simple linear expressions.

▶▶ Construct and solve linear equations.

▶▶ Use the relationship between addition and subtraction.

▶▶ Use the relationship between multiplication and division.

▶▶ Recognise and explain patterns and relationships.

▶▶ Solve a problem by extracting and interpreting data in graphs.

We go round Earth in 90 minutes. That's an average speed of 17 500 miles an hour!

You can calculate many measures using a formula.

Before you start

You should know how to ...

1 Explain a relationship in words.

2 Recognise that subtraction is the inverse of addition.

3 Recognise that division is the inverse of multiplication.

Check in

1 a y is 1 more than x.

  x is 3. What is y?

 b y is twice x.

  x is 4. What is y?

2 Copy and complete these inverse calculations:

 a $16 + 2 = 18$ so $18 - 2 = \_\_$

 b $24 + 5 = \_\_$ so $29 - \_\_ = 5$

 c $12 + \_\_ = 21$ so $21 - 12 = \_\_$

 d $17 - \_\_ = 11$ so $11 + \_\_ = 17$

3 Copy and complete these inverse calculations:

 a $2 \times 3 = 6$ so $6 \div 2 = \_\_$

 b $10 \times 8 = \_\_$ so $80 \div \_\_ = 8$

 c $5 \times \_\_ = 30$ so $30 \div 5 = \_\_$

 d $28 \div \_\_ = 4$ so $4 \times \_\_ = 28$

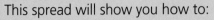

This spread will show you how to:

▶▶ Use brackets.

KEYWORDS
Order   Factorise
Factors   Brackets

When there are 2 operations, you need to do 2 calculations:

$9 \times 2 + 3$

$9 \times 2 = 18$ then $18 + 3 = 21$

Different orders give different answers.

You can use brackets to show the order of calculations.
You do the calculation in the brackets first.

$(9 \times 2) + 3 = 18 + 3$
$= 21$

$9 \times (2 + 3) = 9 \times 5$
$= 45$

This gives the order of operations:
▶ Brackets: ( ).
▶ Powers: 2^2.
▶ Multiplication or Division: × or ÷.
▶ Addition or Subtraction: + or −.

You use this order to work out a calculation.

You can use brackets in formulas.
▶ Perimeter of a
rectangle = length + width + length + width
$= 2 \times$ (length + width)

You work out length + width then multiply by 2.

example

Put brackets into this calculation to make the answer 40:
$4 \times 4 + 5 + 1$.

Try: $4 \times (4 + 5) + 1 = 4 \times 9 + 1$
$= 36 + 1$
$= 37$

$4 \times 10 = 40$ so try to make 10.
Try: $4 \times (4 + 5 + 1) = 4 \times 10$
$= 40$
The answer is $4 \times (4 + 5 + 1)$.

You know that × comes before + so you don't need to try $(4 \times 4) + 5 + 1$.

Exercise A5.1

1 Work out:

Remember to do the calculation in brackets first.

  a $10 \times (2 - 1)$ **b** $5 \times (8 + 2)$ **c** $24 \div (3 + 5)$

  d $(9 - 2) \times 4$ **e** $(8 - 4) \times 2$ **f** $(7 - 3) \times 4$

2 Add brackets to these calculations to make the answers correct.

  a $5 \times 6 - 3 = 15$ **b** $5 \times 6 - 3 = 27$ **c** $12 - 5 \times 3 = 21$

  d $16 \div 2 + 6 = 2$ **e** $16 \div 2 + 6 = 14$ **f** $25 \times 6 - 2 = 100$

3 Work at these calculations using brackets.
The first one is done for you. You can calculate mentally.

  a $3 \times (3 + 7) = 3 \times 10$ **b** $2 \times (4 - 2)$ **c** $5 \times (16 - 10)$
                       $= 30$

  d $10 \times (13 - 8)$ **e** $8 \times (5 - 3)$ **f** $7 \times (24 + 6)$

  g $5 \times (12 - 4)$ **h** $9 \times (7 - 3)$ **i** $2 \times (3 - 5)$

4 Use the formula:

  ▶ perimeter = 2 × (length + width)

to list possible lengths and widths of these rectangles.
The first one is started for you

a

Perimeter = 10 cm

Perimeter = $2 \times (1 + 4)$

b

Perimeter = 14 cm

c

Perimeter = 20 cm

5 Copy and complete these calculations.

  a $3 \times (\underline{} + \underline{}) = 21$ **b** $4 \times (\underline{} - \underline{}) = 20$

  c $2 \times (\underline{} + \underline{}) = 16$ **d** $6 \times (\underline{} + \underline{}) = 18$

  e $2 \times (\underline{} - \underline{}) = 14$ **f** $5 \times (\underline{} + \underline{}) = 35$

6 Use the order of operations to work out these calculations.

  a $4 \times 4 + 5 + 1$ **b** $9 \div 3 \times 2 - 1$

  c $3 + 1 \times 5 - 2$ **d** $3 \times (3 \times 7) - 5$

  e $10 - 3 \times 5 + 5$ **f** $12 + 3 - 10 \div 2$

This spread will show you how to:

▶▶ Develop from explaining a relationship in words to expressing it in a formula using symbols.

▶▶ Substitute positive integers into simple linear expressions.

KEYWORDS

Value   Expression

Substitute   Evaluate

You can use symbols to stand for unknown values.

example

a If you weigh x kg and you lose 3 kg, what will your new weight be?

b If you have x pounds in your wallet and your aunt gives you £10 more, how much will you have altogether?

c If you have x pieces of rock, then cut each piece into 3, how many pieces will you have altogether?

....

a x less 3 kg = $x - 3$ kg

b £x plus £10 = £x + 10

c x pieces × 3 = $3x$ pieces

This is an expression: $4x + 3$.

You call it an expression because it does not have any value.

When you have a value for x then you can **evaluate** the expression.

> Evaluate means work out a value for.

When $x = 5$: $4x + 3 = (4 \times 5) + 3$
$$= 20 + 3$$
$$= 23$$

When $x = 7$: $4x + 3 = (4 \times 7) + 3$
$$= 28 + 3$$
$$= 31$$

example

Evaluate these expressions when $a = 20$.

a $\frac{a}{5} + 6$ **b** $\frac{a}{2} - 4$

....

If $a = 20$:

a $\frac{a}{5} + 6 = \frac{20}{5} + 6$
$$= 4 + 6$$
$$= 10$$

b $\frac{a}{2} - 4 = \frac{20}{2} - 4$
$$= 10 - 4$$
$$= 6$$

Exercise A5.2

1 Write expressions for these questions.

   a I had £x in my wallet. I spent £15 of the money.
How much money do I have now?

   b My dad is 4 times my age. I am y years old.
How old is my dad?

   c Darren scores 3 times as much as me in his test.
I score z%. What is Darren's score?

   d Juliet has m detentions. Amy has 1 more detention than Juliet.
How many detentions does Amy have?

2 Substitute these values into the expressions.

> $x = 4$ $y = 5$ $a = 2$ $z = 1$

   a $y + 3$ **b** $z \times 4$ **c** $y \div 5$ **d** $x + 11$

   e $5x$ **f** $4y$ **g** $10y$ **h** $12z$

3 These expressions have 2 operations.
Substitute the values in question 2 into these expressions.
The first one is done for you

   a $3x + 15 = (3 \times 4) + 15$ **b** $4 + 2z$ **c** $10 - 5a$
                $= 12 + 15 = 27$

   d $5y - 7$ **e** $10x \div 2$ **f** $16 + 8a$

   g $7y \times 2$ **h** $12 \div 3z$ **i** $5x - 2y$

4 ▸ Write an expression for the perimeter of each of these shapes.
   ▸ If $y = 11$ cm and $x = 9$ cm, find the perimeter of each shape.

   a   **b**

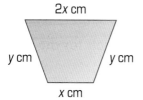

5 John is x years old, his dad is 3 times John's age.

   a Write an expression for John's father's age.

   b If John is 11, how old is John's dad?

6 Claire is twice her brother's age, plus another 4 years.
Her brother is y years old.

   a Write an expression for Claire's age.

   b If Claire is 10, how old is her brother?

This spread will show you how to:

▶▶ Develop from explaining a relationship in words to expressing it in a formula using symbols.

▶▶ Substitute positive integers into simple formulas.

KEYWORDS

Expression   Evaluate

Value   Formula

Alice is doing a Science investigation.

As she adds weight to the spring its height above the floor decreases.

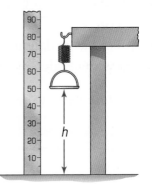

She makes a formula that links the weight on the spring and its height above the floor.

This is Alice's formula:

▶ Height = 80 − (30 + 3 × weight)

She can use her formula to calculate the height of the weight above the floor when she adds different weights.

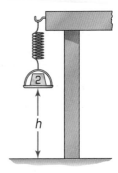

example

Alice puts a 5 kg weight onto the spring.
What is its height above the floor?

You can write it out in full:

Height = 80 − (30 + 3 × weight)

     = 80 − (30 + 3 × 5)

     = 80 − (30 + 15)

     = 80 − 45

     = 35 cm

You can also use symbols for the height and weight.

$h \rightarrow$ height $w \rightarrow$ weight.

$h = 80 - (30 + 3w)$

$h = 80 - (30 + 3 \times 5)$

$h = 80 - (30 + 15)$

$h = 80 - 45$

$h = 35$ cm

> $3w$ means $3 \times w$

Exercise A5.3

1 Evaluate this expression for different weights: $30 + (3 \times \text{weight})$
The first one is done for you.

a weight = 4 kg:
$$30 + (3 \times \text{weight}) = 30 + 3 \times 4$$
$$= 30 + 12$$
$$= 42$$

b weight = 6 kg   **c** weight = 2 kg   **d** weight = 11 kg   **e** weight = 14 kg

2 Use Alice's formula to calculate the heights of the spring above the floor with these weights.

▶ Height = $80 - (30 + 3 \times \text{weight})$

> Calculate the value of the bracket first.

The first one is done for you.

a weight is 1 kg
$$\text{bracket} \rightarrow 30 + (3 \times 1)$$
$$= 30 + 3$$
$$= 33$$
$$\text{Height} = 80 - 33$$
$$= 47 \text{ cm}$$

b weight = 10 kg   **c** weight = 12 kg   **d** weight = 6 kg
e weight = 15 kg   **f** weight = 8 kg   **g** weight = 16 kg

3 This is a different formula.
It calculates the area of a triangle.

$$A = \frac{\text{height} \times \text{base}}{2} \text{ or } \frac{h \times b}{2}$$

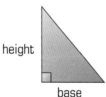

Use this formula to calculate the areas of these triangles. The first one is done for you

a

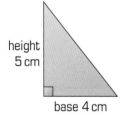

height 5 cm
base 4 cm

$$\text{Area} = \frac{\text{height} \times \text{base}}{2}$$
$$A = \frac{5 \times 4}{2} = \frac{20}{2}$$
$$\text{Area} = 10 \text{ cm}^2$$

b

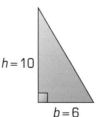

$h = 10$
$b = 6$

c

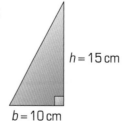

$h = 15$ cm
$b = 10$ cm

> Remember that the units of this area are cm^2.

This spread will show you how to:

▶▶ Use the relationship between addition and subtraction.
▶▶ Develop from explaining a relationship in words to expressing it in a formula using symbols.
▶▶ Construct and solve linear equations.

KEYWORDS
Equation
Inverse operation

You can solve an equation using inverse operations.
Sometimes you can simplify the equation first.

This equation has brackets: $(12 \times 2) + 3 = x + 10$
First you work out the bracket: $24 + 3 = x + 10$
$27 = x + 10$

Now you can use inverse operations.

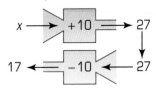

So $x = 17$.

▶ The inverse of + is −.

▶ The inverse of − is +.

example

A piece of string is exactly 23 cm long.
A piece of the string 9 cm long is cut off.
How much is left?

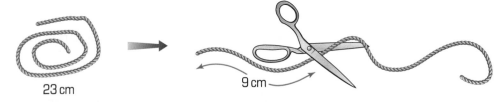

23 cm   9 cm

Give the length of the string left a symbol: y
Now make an equation from what you know:

You know that: the total length is $y + 9$ cm.
                          the total length is 23 cm.

So, $y + 9 = 23$
$y = 23 - 9$ (the inverse of add 9 is subtract 9)
$y = 14$ cm

Exercise A5.4

1 Copy these equations and fill in the missing numbers so that both sides have an equal value.

  a $42 - 20 = 2 + \underline{\quad}$

  b $6 + 19 = \underline{\quad} + 10$

  c $6 \times 6 = \underline{\quad} - 3$

  d $50 \div 2 = \underline{\quad} + 11$

2 Solve these equations to find the value of each letter.
Show all your working.

  a $7 + (3 \times 10) = x$ **b** $9 + (5 \times 7) = x$ **c** $(5 \times 8) + t = 45$

  d $w - (56 \div 7) = 2$ **e** $h + (7 \times 3) = 33$ **f** $(4 \times 6) - a = 12$

  g $(8 \times 4) + q = 50$ **h** $s + (30 \div 6) = 21$ **i** $n - (6 \times 3) = 22$

3 These 2 pieces of string are the same length.
They are both 42 cm long.
A piece has been cut off the second string.
The piece is 19 cm long.

       42 cm   19 cm   *p* cm

  a Write an equation using p that links the lengths of both pieces of string.

  b Solve the equation to find the length of p.

4 The lengths of wood used to make these bookshelves are the same.
They are each cut into 3 pieces to make a middle and 2 ends.

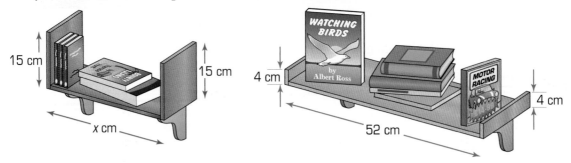

  a Write down the length of wood used to make each shelf.

  b Use your answers to write an equation that links the lengths of the wood used.

  c Solve the equation to find the length x.

This spread will show you how to:

▶▶ Use the relationship between multiplication and division.
▶▶ Develop from explaining a relationship in words to expressing it in a formula using symbols.
▶▶ Construct and solve simple linear equations.

These 3 boxes are equal in weight.
Together they weigh 15 kg.

You write:
$$3n = 15$$

$n \longrightarrow \boxed{\times 3} \Longrightarrow 15$

The inverse of multiply by 3 is divide by 3.

$5 \longleftarrow \boxed{\div 3} \longleftarrow 15$

Each box must be $15 \div 3 = 5$ kg.

▶ The inverse of × is ÷.

▶ The inverse of ÷ is ×.

example

The weight of all the boxes is x kg.
$\frac{1}{4}$ of the boxes weighs 5 kg.
Find the weight of all the boxes together.

$\boxed{\frac{1}{4}x} \quad \boxed{\frac{1}{4}x}$
$\boxed{\frac{1}{4}x} \quad \boxed{\frac{1}{4}x}$

....

The equation for the balance is $\frac{1}{4}x = 5$.
$\frac{1}{4}$ of x means x divided by 4.

$x \longrightarrow \boxed{\div 4} \Longrightarrow 5$

The inverse of divide by 4 is multiply by 4.

$20 \longleftarrow \boxed{\times 4} \longleftarrow 5$

The weight of all the boxes together is 20 kg.

Exercise A5.5

1 Copy these pairs of equations and fill in the missing numbers.

    a $3 \times 8 =$ ___ $24 \div$ ___ $= 3$ **b** $5 \times 9 =$ ___ $45 \div$ ___ $= 9$

    c $12 \times 9 =$ ___   ___ $\div 12 =$ ____

2 Solve these equations using inverses to find the value of each letter.
The first one is started for you.

    a $3n = 12$ $12 \div 3 =$ ___   so $n =$ ___

    b $4x = 16$ **c** $2p = 20$ **d** $18q = 3$

    e $9n = 45$ **f** $3t = 21$ **g** $12d = 96$

3 Copy and complete these sentences.

    a $\frac{1}{4}$ of an amount means divide the amount by ___.

    b $\frac{1}{3}$ of an amount means divide the amount by ___.

    c $\frac{1}{10}$ of an amount means divide the amount by ___.

    d $\frac{1}{5}$ of an amount means _____ the amount by ___.

4 Write these sentences as fractions. The first one is done for you.

    a x divided by 3 is $\frac{1}{3}x$.   **b** m divided by 6 is ___

    c y divided by 5 is ___   **d** g divided by 9 is ___

5 Copy and complete these inverse machines. The first one is done for you

    a $\frac{1}{3}x$ 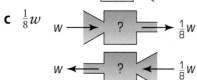   **b** $\frac{1}{6}y$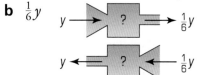

    c $\frac{1}{8}w$ 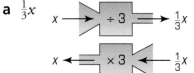   **d** $\frac{1}{10}a$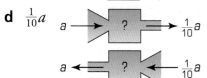

6 Use inverse machines to solve the equations and find the value
of the whole symbol. The first one is done for you.

    a $\frac{1}{3}x = 4$ **b** $\frac{1}{4}a = 15$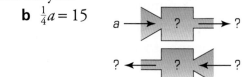

    So $x = 12$

    c $\frac{1}{8}t = 5$ **d** $\frac{1}{10}b = 7$

KEYWORDS
Formula
Graph

This spread will show you how to:

▶▶ Recognise and explain patterns and relationships.
▶▶ Solve a problem by extracting and interpreting graphs.

Each of these dice games has different rules to win.

Game 1

The score on the red dice must equal the score on the white dice.

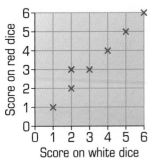

All the winning scores have red crosses.
The winning formula is:

red score = white score

$$r = w$$

The blue cross is at (2, 3).
This is not a winner because the red score is 1 more than the white score

Game 2

The score on the red dice must be 1 less than the score on the white dice.

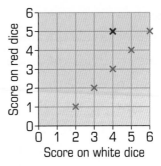

All the winning scores have green crosses.
The winning formula this time is:

red score = white score − 1

$$r = w - 1$$

The purple cross is at (4, 5).
This is not a winner because the red score is 1 more than the white score.

You can use a formula to describe a graph.

example

This graph shows the cost of buying icecreams.
a Write a formula to describe the graph.
b If you have £5 to spend how many icecreams can you buy?

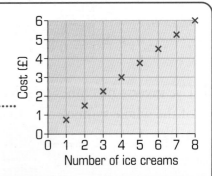

a Cost = 0.75 × number of icecreams.
 You can write this as: $c = 0.75n$
b From the graph, £5 would give you 6 icecreams with some money left over.

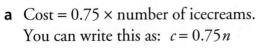

You would have 50p left as 6 icecreams cost £4.50, and 5 − 4.50 = 0.5.

Exercise A5.6

1 Write the formulas for each of these games. Use the symbols *r* and *w*.
Start your formulas: *r* = _____.

a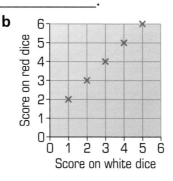

b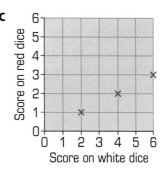

c

2 This graph shows the cost of hiring DVDs.

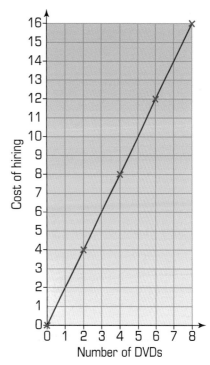

a Write the formula to describe the graph.
Start with:
Cost = _____ × number of DVDs.
b How much will you pay to hire 6 DVDs?
c If you have £6 to spend how many DVDs can you hire?
d Calculate the cost of hiring 10 DVDs.

3 Another company sells CDs for 40p each.
They charge £1 delivery for each order.
a Write the formula to describe the cost. Start with: Cost = _____
b Use your formula to copy and complete this table.

Number of CDs	1	2	3	4	5	6	10
Cost (£)	1.40			2.60			5

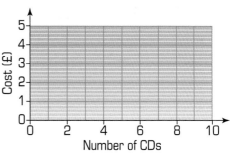

c Draw axes like these on graph paper and plot the values from the table.
d Use your graph to find the total cost, including delivery, of:
i 7 CDs   **ii** 8 CDs   **iii** 9 CDs.

You should know how to ...

1 Develop from explaining a relationship in words to expressing it in a formula using symbols.
- ▶ $x + 1$ means 1 more than x.
- ▶ $y - 2$ means 2 less than y.
- ▶ $3a$ means 3 lots of a or $3 \times a$.
- ▶ $\frac{d}{4}$ means d divided by 4 or $d \div 4$.

2 Substitute positive integers into simple linear expressions.

3 Construct and solve linear equations.

Check out

1 Write an expression for each of these questions.

a Sarah has x sweets.
Emily has 4 more sweets than Sarah.
How many sweets does Emily have?

b Tom has y sweets.
He eats 3 of his sweets.
How many sweets does Tom have left?

c Lauren has z sweets.
Jack has twice as many sweets as Lauren.
How many sweets does Jack have?

2 Work out the value of the expression $4n - 3$ when:
a $n = 1$
b $n = 8$
c $n = 0$
d $n = 4$

3 Pete earns £T every hour.
He works for h hours.
The amount of money he earns is W.
a Write a formula for W in terms of T and h.
b If $T = 5$ and $h = 15$, calculate W.

3 Statistical reports

This unit will show you how to:

▶▶ Plan and collect data.

▶▶ Construct frequency tables with given equal class intervals for sets of discrete data.

▶▶ Find the mode and range of a set of data.

▶▶ Find the median and mean of a set of data.

▶▶ Construct and use stem-and-leaf diagrams.

▶▶ Solve a problem by representing, extracting and interpreting data in tables, graphs and charts.

What shall we produce next?

We'll have to give choices, we can't produce just **anything**.

Let's ask our customers.

You have to think carefully before you start to research.

Before you start

You should know how to …

1 Read data in a frequency table.

Check in

1 The table shows the number of cups of tea and coffee drunk by Helen in a week.

Day of week	Mon	Tue	Wed	Thur	Fri	Sat	Sun
Cups of tea	3	5	2	4	2	3	4
Cups of coffee	2	2	3	2	3	2	2

a How many cups of coffee did Helen drink on Thursday?

b On which days did Helen drink more coffee than tea?

c On which day did Helen drink the most tea?

d How many cups of tea did Helen drink in the week?

2 Order numbers.

2 Write these sets of numbers in order, starting with the smallest.

a 6, 8, 2, 4, 9, 11

b 45, 23, 33, 42, 29, 37, 22

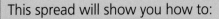

This spread will show you how to:

▶▶ Plan how to collect data.
▶▶ Construct frequency tables with given equal class intervals for sets of discrete data.

KEYWORDS
Sample size
Hypothesis
Frequency table
Primary data
Secondary data

Sharon's hypothesis is that boys are taller than girls.

She collects primary data by doing a survey at school.

Sharon measures the height of 20 boys and 20 girls from each Year.
There are 5 Years so the sample size is $20 \times 2 \times 5 = 200$ students.

She looks for secondary data on the internet.

She downloads data from different websites. She is careful that the data is relevant to her investigation. The sample size of this data is much larger.

▶ Primary data is data you collect yourself.

▶ Secondary data has already been collected for you.

Here are Sharon's results for Year 9.

Girls	Height in cm	Boys
I	80 – 99	
ЖЖ	100 – 119	III
ЖЖ IIII	120 – 139	ЖЖ II
ЖЖ	140 – 159	ЖЖ III
	160 – 179	II
	180 – 199	

The results are grouped in intervals of 20 cm.
She shows this data on a bar chart.

Here are some relevant data Sharon found on a website. Source: www.cdc.gov

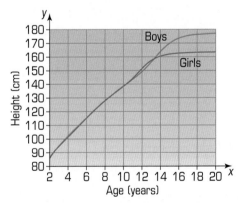

Graph showing the mean average heights of boys and girls from 2 to 20 years old.

Exercise D3.1

1 Here are some websites that Sharon found.
Which websites could be useful in her research?
   a **Amazing humans**. Facts about human achievement and endurance.
   b **Human growth 1**. Studies by the California Institute on growth disorders.
   c **Human growth 2**. Statistics on average growth rates of boys and girls aged
                          3 years to 20 years.
   d **New heights**. History of manned flight into space.
   e **Child development**. Health Council figures on child development
                            including data on average height and weight.

2 Here are the heights of 20 girls in Year 8.
They have been written out in order.

> This is discrete data – the objects or events can be counted.

| 110 cm | 124 cm | 125 cm | 128 cm | 134 cm | 135 cm | 137 cm | 138 cm | 139 cm | 140 cm |
| 142 cm | 144 cm | 146 cm | 149 cm | 150 cm | 153 cm | 154 cm | 158 cm | 162 cm | 180 cm |

Copy this frequency table and fill in the tally data.
Then fill in the frequency data.

Height in cm	Girls	Frequency
100–119		
120–139		
140–159		
160–179		
180–199		

3 Sharon measures the height of 20 boys in Year 8.
The results have been written out in order.

| 118 cm | 130 cm | 135 cm | 136 cm | 138 cm | 142 cm | 144 cm | 149 cm | 150 cm | 154 cm |
| 158 cm | 159 cm | 163 cm | 164 cm | 164 cm | 167 cm | 168 cm | 170 cm | 173 cm | 177 cm |

   a Group the data on a frequency table.
   b Display this data on a bar chart.

4 Sue asked a group of her friends to record how many text messages
they sent in 1 evening. Here are her results:

1	3	0	5	8	4	0	4	6	3
3	4	6	4	2	7	6	4	6	1
5	7	5	4	9	0	8	2	5	7

She organises her results in a table like this.
Use the data to draw a table, and fill in the
frequencies.

Number of calls	Frequency
0–1	
2–3	

This spread will show you how to:

▶▶ Find the mode and range of a set of data.
▶▶ Find the median and mean of a set of data.

KEYWORDS

Statistics   Mean
Mode   Range
Median

You can make sense of your data with statistics.

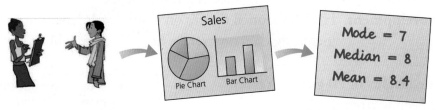

You collect data.   You organise and   You calculate averages to
                       display the data.   make sense of the data.

▶ Mean = total of the values divided by the number of values.

example

This table shows the number of pets that students have at home.
Find the mean number of pets per student.

Number of pets	1	2	3	4	5
Number of students	5	6	4	4	1

5 students have 1 pet = 5 × 1 = 5 pets
6 students have 2 pets = 6 × 2 = 12 pets
4 students have 3 pets = 4 × 3 = 12 pets
4 students have 4 pets = 4 × 4 = 16 pets
1 student has 5 pets   = 1 × 5 = 5 pets
 ̄20 ̄   ̄50 ̄

There are 50 pets in total.
There are 20 students.
50 ÷ 20 = 2.5

The mean number of pets per student is 2.5.

▶ The mode is the most common value.
  4, 5, 7, 8, 8, 8, 8, 10, 11, 11 14 ⟶ The mode is 8.

▶ The median is the middle value when the data are in order.
  10, 13, 16, 22, 25, 27, 34 ⟶ The median is 22.
                ▲

▶ The range is the difference between the largest and smallest values.
  5, 8, 9, 9, 14, 16, 18 ⟶ 18 − 5 = 13 ⟶ The range is 13.

Exercise D3.2

1 This data has been put in order, smallest to largest.
  a What is the mode?
  b What is the median?
  c What is the range?

Scores from 2 dice thrown 20 times
2 5 5 6 7 7 7 7 7 8
8 8 9 9 9 10 11 11 11 12

2 a Write this data in order, smallest to largest.

Scores from 20 throws of a dart
12 15 3 5 60 10 20 10 12 1
14 19 1 17 39 15 10 20 19 10

  b What is the mode?
  c What is the median?
  d What is the range?

3 What is the mean of each of these sets of data?
  a 3, 10, 5, 1, 6
  b 2, 4, 4, 7, 2, 5, 4
  c 60, 40, 30, 20, 20, 50, 10, 40, 20, 30

4 Here are the results of a survey to find out how many phones people had in their homes.

Number of phones	1	2	3	4
Number of people	10	3	6	2

  a How many people had 3 phones?
  b How many people had 1 phone?
  c How many people were asked for this survey?
  d How many phones did the people own altogether?
  e Find the mean number of phones per person.

5 A group of parents are asked how many children they each have.
Here are the results:

Number of children	1	2	3	4	5	6
Number of parents	5	10	5	1	2	1

Find the mean number of children per parent.

This spread will show you how to:

▶▶ Construct and use stem-and-leaf diagrams.
▶▶ Find the mode and range of a set of data.
▶▶ Find the median of a set of data.

KEYWORDS

Stem-and-leaf diagram
Order   Range
Key   Median
Partition   Modal

▶ A stem-and-leaf diagram makes it easier to find averages.

Sharon draws a stem-and-leaf diagram to record the heights of students in class 9C.
She writes the heights out in order:

143 cm	148 cm	149 cm	152 cm	152 cm	154 cm	155 cm	158 cm
159 cm	160 cm	163 cm	164 cm	167 cm	167 cm	167 cm	168 cm
168 cm	169 cm	170 cm	171 cm	173 cm	175 cm	177 cm	179 cm

She puts this data onto a stem-and-leaf diagram.

A stem-and-leaf diagram works by partitioning.

$143 = 140 + 3$

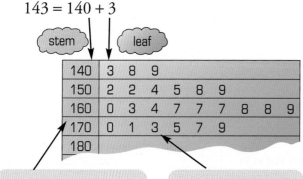

stem	leaf							
140	3	8	9					
150	2	2	4	5	8	9		
160	0	3	4	7	7	7	8	8	9
170	0	1	3	5	7	9		
180								

Key:
140 | 3 stands for 143 cm

You must use a key to explain your scale.

The stem organises the data into 10 cm groups.

The leaves show the rest of each number.

▶ The range: The smallest height is 143 cm and the tallest height is 179 cm.
The range is 179 – 143 = 36 cm.

▶ The modal height is the most common height: 167 cm

▶ The biggest group is heights between 160 cm and 169 cm.
This is the modal group.

▶ The median: There are 24 pieces of data.
The middle value is between the 12th value (164 cm)
and the 13th value (166 cm).
The median is 165 cm.

Exercise D3.3

1 This stem-and-leaf diagram shows the number of merits awarded to students in class 9S.

   a How many students are there in class 9S?

   b How many students earned 77 merits?

   c How many students earned 30 merits?

   d What is the range of this data?

   e What is the modal number of merits?

   f What is the median number of merits?

Merits awarded to 9S						
20	2	7	7	9		
30	0	0	1	8	9	
40	1	4	6	6	6	6	8
50	2	7	9			
60	0	3	5	6		
70	4	7	7	7	9	
80	3	8				

Key : 80|8 stands for 88

2 This table shows the results of a recent Maths test.

7	9	14	16	20	23	29	31
34	34	34	34	36	38	40	42
44	45	47	47	49	51	53	55

   a The stem of the diagram is drawn for you. Copy and complete the stem-and-leaf diagram for these results.

   b What is the modal score for the Maths test?

   c What is the range of the scores?

Maths test results	
0	
10	
20	
30	
40	
50	

Key :50|5 stands for 55

3 Ricky asked 25 people to record the number of text messages they sent in 1 month.
Here are the totals in order:

   a Show these totals on a stem-and-leaf diagram.

      You need to:

      ▸ Draw the stem of the diagram.

      ▸ Partition the numbers and put them on the right stem.

      ▸ Draw a key to explain the scale.

   b What is the range of the data?

   c What is the modal group?

   d What is the median value?

12,	17,	19,				
20,	24,	28,				
33,	35,	36,	37,	37,	38,	39,
44,	47,	48,	49,			
50,	55,	59,				
62,	65,	67,				
74,						
81						

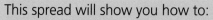

This spread will show you how to:

▶▶ Solve a problem by representing, extracting and interpreting data in tables, graphs and charts.

Bar chart

The easiest way to display discrete data is to use a bar chart.

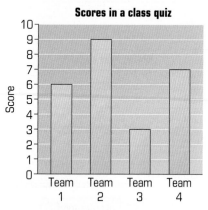

The teams scored 6 + 9 + 3 + 7 = 25 points altogether.
The range is 6 points.

Stem-and-leaf diagram

A stem-and-leaf diagram uses partitioning to show data.

20 students record how many text messages they send in 1 day						
10	0	6	6	9		
20	1	3	7	7	7	8	9
30	0	1	5	8		
40	2	6	7			
50	3	7				

Key: 50|7 stands for 57

The lowest value is 10 messages.
The highest value is 57 messages.
The range is 47.
The modal group is 20–29.

▶ Discrete data are data that can be counted.

Pictogram

A clear and simple way to display data is to use a pictogram.

▶ 15 bags of beef crisps were sold.
▶ Each whole symbol represents 10 bags.
▶ Plain crisps were the most popular.

Crisps sold in railway canteen in 1 day

Beef   Chicken   Plain   Bacon

Exercise D3.4

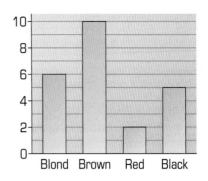

1 The bar chart shows the hair colour of students in class 9P.

a How many students have red hair?

b Which is the modal colour?

c How many students are there in 9P altogether?

2 The table shows the colours of cars parked in the school car park.

Red	Silver	Black	Blue	Green
3	8	5	2	1

Draw a bar chart to show this data.

Remember to add labels to your bar chart.

3 ▶ You can sort data more quickly by using a rough version of a stem-and-leaf diagram first:

1. Partition the data into groups you are using on the stem.
2. Put the data on the right stem, in any order.

140	9	3	2	5

3. Sort the leaf into the right order.

140	2	3	5	9

In a training session, rugby players have to do press-ups for 1 minute.
Here are the number of press-ups each player did, in order.

a Show this data on a stem-and-leaf diagram.

b What is the range?

c What is the median?

d Which is the modal group in your diagram?

27	29	32	33	37
37	38	40	41	44
45	45	45	48	49
52	56	57	60	66

4 The pictogram shows the sales of bottled drinks from a corner shop in 1 week.

a Which drink sells the most?

b How many bottles of Cola were sold?

c Which drink sold 30 bottles?

d Which drink sold the least?

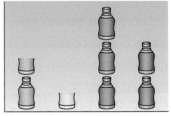

Key:
⊔ = 10
🍾 = 20

Orange Lemon Cola Water

5 Display this data on a pictogram.

▶ Decide on a symbol to represent groups of data.

▶ Decide the value of each symbol.

▶ Draw the pictogram and key.

▶ Give the pictogram a title.

Sales of newspapers at a newsagent

The Gazette	The Press	The News	The Comet
25	10	35	45

This spread will show you how to:

▶▶ Solve a problem by representing, extracting and interpreting data in tables, graphs and charts.

Line graph

A line graph shows a trend over time.

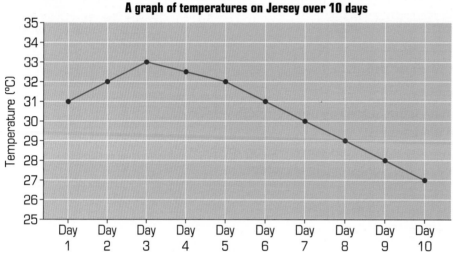

A graph of temperatures on Jersey over 10 days

You join points with a line when they show a range over time.

▶ The temperature on Day 8 is 29 °C.
▶ The hottest day is Day 3.
▶ The trend is that it gets cooler after Day 3.

Pie chart

A pie chart uses parts of a circle to show data.
You can compare the size of each category with the whole of the data.

▶ The most common reason for breakdowns is electrical.
▶ The least common reason for breakdowns is brakes.
▶ If there were 40 breakdowns, about 10 of them would be due to engines.

Engines ~ $\frac{1}{4}$ of the whole pie.
$\frac{1}{4}$ of 40 = 40 ÷ 4 = 10.

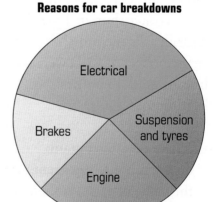

Reasons for car breakdowns

Exercise D3.5

1 The line graph shows the growth rate of the world's tallest man, Robert Wadlow from 9 to 18 years old.

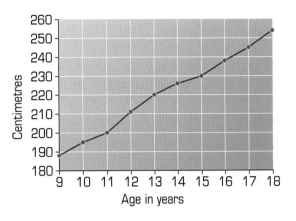

a How tall was Robert Wadlow when he was:

    i 11 years   **ii** 15 years   **iii** 18 years?

b How old was Robert Wadlow when he was 195 cm tall?

c How many centimetres did he grow between the age of 11 and 15?

2 Stanley's weight is measured in kilograms each year on his birthday. Here are the measurements for his first 8 birthdays.

Year	1	2	3	4	5	6	7	8
Weight (kg)	6	9	11	12	16	18	23	24

a Draw a line graph to show this data.

b What did Stanley weigh when he was 3 years old?

c What age was Stanley when he weighed 16 kg?

d Between which 2 years did Stanley put on the most weight?

3 Class 8T and 8W are asked to vote for their favourite ice cream flavour.

These pie charts show the results.

  a Which is the favourite flavour in 8T?

  b Which is the favourite flavour in 8W?

  c In which class was raspberry more popular?

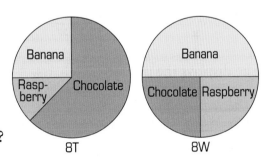

4 Lyn draws a pie chart to show how she spends her day.

  a Does Lyn spend more time working or sleeping?

  b Does Lyn spend more time travelling or shopping?

  c Which activity does Lyn spend least time on?

  d A day lasts for 24 hours. Roughly how long does Lyn sleep for?

  e Roughly how long does Lyn work for each day?

This spread will show you how to:
▶▶ Interpret the results of a statistical enquiry.
▶▶ Compare 2 distributions.

Sharon investigated the hypothesis that: boys are taller than girls.
Here is the data she collected on 20 Year 7 boys and 20 Year 7 girls.

Girls				
98 cm	109 cm	112 cm	115 cm	117 cm
119 cm	121 cm	122 cm	125 cm	130 cm
134 cm	135 cm	136 cm	138 cm	139 cm
144 cm	147 cm	150 cm	153 cm	158 cm

Boys				
110 cm	117 cm	118 cm	120 cm	128 cm
130 cm	133 cm	134 cm	136 cm	138 cm
144 cm	145 cm	146 cm	148 cm	153 cm
155 cm	157 cm	158 cm	161 cm	165 cm

By comparing this data she can begin to produce some statistics.

▶ The range is 60 cm for girls and 55 cm for boys.
▶ The median for girls is 132 cm and 141 cm for boys.

Sharon groups the data onto a frequency table.
She groups the data in 20 cm intervals.

Girls		Height in cm	Boys	
Frequency	Tally		Tally	Frequency
1	I	80–99		0
5	JHT	100–119	III	3
9	JHT IIII	120–139	JHT II	7
5	JHT	140–159	JHT III	8
0		160–179	II	2

She displays the data on bar charts.

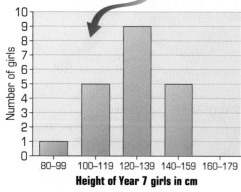

Height of Year 7 girls in cm

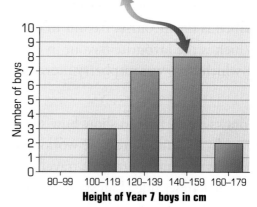

Height of Year 7 boys in cm

From the frequency table and bar charts, Sharon can see that:

▶ The **modal group** for girls is 120 to 139 cm.
▶ The **modal group** for boys is 140 to 159 cm.

From the data, Sharon concludes that boys in Year 7 are, on average, taller than the girls.

Exercise D3.6

1 This is the data Sharon recorded on 20 Year 9 girls and 20 Year 9 boys.

Girls
138 cm 151 cm 152 cm 154 cm 156 cm 157 cm 159 cm 160 cm 162 cm 163 cm
165 cm 165 cm 166 cm 167 cm 168 cm 169 cm 171 cm 172 cm 174 cm 178 cm

Boys
150 cm 154 cm 156 cm 157 cm 159 cm 161 cm 161 cm 162 cm 162 cm 166 cm
168 cm 168 cm 169 cm 171 cm 172 cm 174 cm 175 cm 178 cm 180 cm 182 cm

a What is the range for girls?   **b** What is the range for boys?

c What is the median for girls?   **d** What is the median for boys?

2 Copy and complete this frequency table and using the data about Year 9 students.

The group intervals are 10 centimetres.

Girls			Boys		
Frequency	Tally	Height in cm	Tally	Frequency	
		130–139			
		140–149			
		150–159			
		160–169			
		170–179			
		180–189			

a What is the modal group for girls?

b What is the modal group for boys?

c Draw a bar chart from the data on the frequency table.

d Using the data and statistics, write a sentence about the height of boys and girls in Year 9.

3 Sharon calculates the mean average height for boys and girls in Years 7, 8 and 9.
This data is shown on this table.

	Girls	Boys
Year 7	130.1 cm	139.8 cm
Year 8	142.4 cm	152.9 cm
Year 9	162.3 cm	166.2 cm

a What is the difference in the mean average height between:

   i girls and boys in Year 7?

   ii girls in Year 7 and girls in Year 9?

c Are boys in Year 7 taller, on average, than girls in Year 8?

d A student in Year 9 is 162 cm tall.

Sharon says: "The student **must** be a girl because the mean average height for girls is 162.3 cm".

Why is she wrong?

You should know how to ...

1 Solve a problem by representing, extracting and interpreting data in tables, graphs and charts.

2 Find the mode and range of a set of data.

3 Find the median and mean of a set of data.

Check out

1 Here are the marks on a Maths test sat by Class 9C.

Marks	Frequency
1–20	2
21–40	5
41–60	14
61–80	8
81–100	1

   a Draw a bar chart to show this data.

   b How many students are there in Class 9C?

   c What is the modal group of marks?

2 Find the mode and range of these sets of data.

   a 3, 6, 3, 8, 2, 4, 8, 9, 11, 3

   b 45, 23, 42, 33, 42, 29, 37, 22

   c 54, 32, 74, 22, 93, 18, 64, 22, 73

3 Find the median and mean of these sets of data.

   a 5, 8, 8, 9, 10

   b 14, 7, 3, 16, 10

   c 3, 10, 9, 2, 4, 8

Applying geometrical reasoning

This unit will show you how to:

- ▶▶ Recognise where a shape will be after a translation or rotation.
- ▶▶ Calculate angles around a point.
- ▶▶ Use 2-D representations to visualise 3-D shapes.
- ▶▶ Begin to use plans and elevations.

- ▶▶ Use the formula for the volume of a cuboid.
- ▶▶ Calculate the surface area of a cuboid.
- ▶▶ Construct nets of cuboids.
- ▶▶ Construct nets of solid shapes.
- ▶▶ Visualise 3-D shapes from 2-D diagrams.

Boxes come in all shapes and sizes.

Before you start

You should know how to ...

1 Recognise shapes.

2 Find the area of a rectangle.

Check in

1 What are the names of these shapes?

a   b   c   d

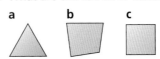

2 Find the areas of these rectangles.

a   b

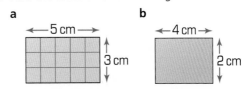

←5 cm→   3 cm   ←4 cm→   2 cm

This spread will show you how to:

▶▶ Recognise where a shape will be after a translation or rotation.

▶▶ Calculate angles around a point.

KEYWORDS

Tessellation   Congruent
Rotation   Translation

This shape is repeated to make a tessellation.

> ▶ A tessellation is a tiling pattern with no gaps or overlaps.

▶ The shapes are congruent.

▶ There are no gaps between the shapes.

Congruent shapes are exactly the same shape and size.

▶ This tessellation is made from translations and rotations.

▶ Not all shapes tessellate.

All triangles tessellate.   All quadrilaterals tessellate.

> ▶ Angles round a point add up to 360°.

The 4 angles where the shapes of the tessellation meet add up to 360°.

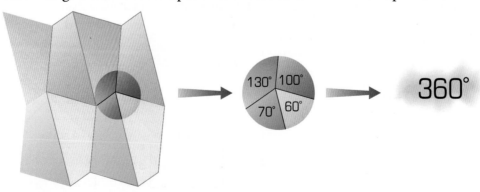

130° | 100°
70° | 60°

360°

red + blue + green + yellow = 360°.

Exercise S4.1

1 Copy this tessellation onto squared paper, and continue it by repeating the shape 5 more times.

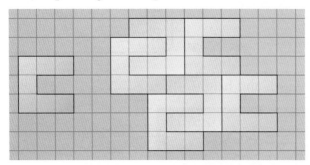

2 Copy these shapes onto squared paper.
Make a tessellation with each shape, using translations and rotations.

a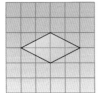 **b**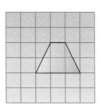 **c** **d**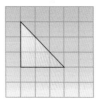

3 Use angle facts you know to work out these angles.
The first one is done for you.

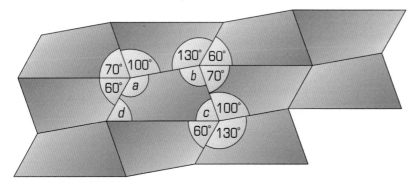

a Angle a

$$a + 60° + 70° + 100° = 360°$$
$$a + 230° = 360°$$
$$a = 130°$$

b Angle b **c** Angle c **d** Angle d

This spread will show you how to:
▸▸ Use 2-D representations to visualise 3-D shapes.
▸▸ Begin to use plans and elevations.

KEYWORDS
3-D   Elevation
Plan

Solid shapes have 3 dimensions: length, width and height.

height

length   width

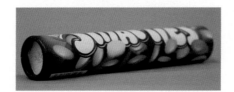

This tube is a cylinder. Its front elevation is circular.

You can look at this shape from 3 different directions:

The top   The front   The side

Plan view   Front elevation   Side elevation

example

Draw the plan view, the side elevation and the front elevation of this shape.

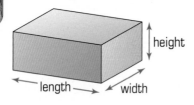

This shape is drawn on isometric paper.

front

The plan view –
look from above.

The side elevation –
look from the side.

The front elevation –
look from the front.

Exercise S4.2

1 Match each of these solids with its plan view (the view from above).

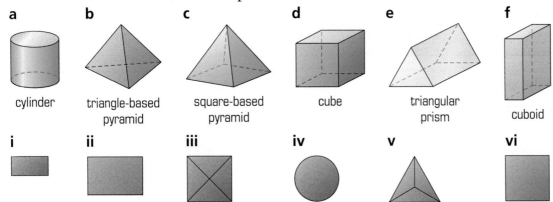

a cylinder
b triangle-based pyramid
c square-based pyramid
d cube
e triangular prism
f cuboid

i   ii   iii   iv   v   vi

2 Match each shape with the drawing of its elevation (the view from the side).

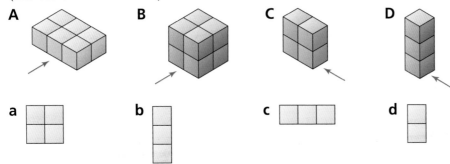

A   B   C   D

a   b   c   d

3 On squared paper, draw the plan view, side elevation and front elevation of each shape.

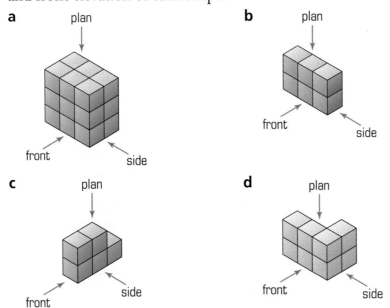

a   plan   front   side

b   plan   front   side

c   plan   front   side

d   plan   front   side

This spread will show you how to:

▶▶ Use the formula for the volume of a cuboid.

KEYWORDS
Volume   Cuboid
Dimensions

A solid shape has 3 dimensions – length, width and height.

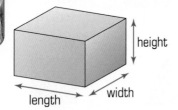

height

length   width

A cuboid is a box.

▶ **The volume of a cuboid is the amount of space it takes up.**

Volume is measured in cubes.

Small volumes are measured in centimetre cubes – cm^3.

1 cm   1 cm

1 cm

A 1 centimetre cube

Large volumes are measured in metre cubes – m^3.

1 m   1 m

1 m

A 1 metre cube

▶ **The volume of a cuboid = length × width × height**

example

Find the volume of this cuboid.

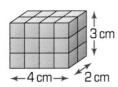

3 cm

←4 cm→   2 cm

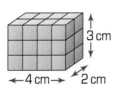

3 cm

←4 cm→   2 cm

$$= 4 \times 2 \times 3 = 24 \text{ cm}^3 =$$

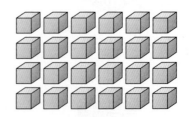

The volume of the box is 24 centimetre cubes.

Exercise S4.3

1 Find the volume of each cuboid.

Give your answers in centimetre cubes – cm³

a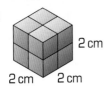
2 cm
2 cm 2 cm

b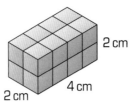
2 cm
2 cm 4 cm

c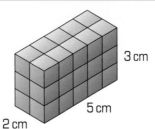
3 cm
2 cm 5 cm

2 Ahmed measures the dimensions of 5 cuboids.
Here are his results.
Using the formula:

Volume = length × width × height

write the volume of each cuboid.

Cuboid	Length	Width	Height	Volume – cm³
1	5 cm	2 cm	1 cm	
2	3 cm	3 cm	2 cm	
3	10 cm	2 cm	3 cm	
4	4 cm	2 cm	5 cm	
5	4 cm	2 cm	10 cm	

3 **a** Draw this cuboid on isometric paper.
b Work out its volume.

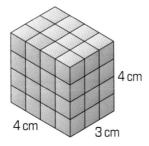
4 cm
4 cm 3 cm

4 Work out the volume of each cuboid.

a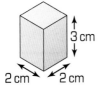
3 cm
2 cm 2 cm

b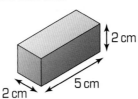
2 cm
2 cm 5 cm

c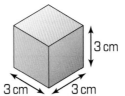
3 cm
3 cm 3 cm

d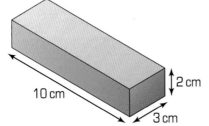
10 cm
2 cm
3 cm

e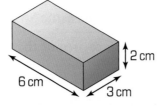
2 cm
6 cm 3 cm

f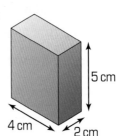
5 cm
4 cm 2 cm

This spread will show you how to:

▶▶ Calculate the surface area of a cuboid.

KEYWORDS

Cuboid   Surface area

Net   Face

A cuboid has 3 dimensions – length, width and height.

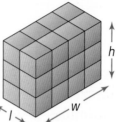

The net of this cuboid shows that it has 6 faces.

The opposite faces have the same area.

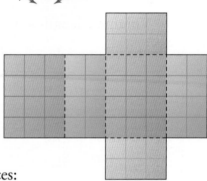

You find the area of the net by adding the areas of the faces:

$8 + 8 + 12 + 12 + 6 + 6 = 52$ cm^2

▶ The area of the net is the same as the surface area of the cuboid.

---

example

Find the surface area of this cuboid:

Area of red face = 6 cm^2 Area of blue face = 4 cm^2 Area of yellow face = 6 cm^2

Opposite face to red   Opposite face to blue   Opposite face to yellow
is the same area = 6 cm^2 is the same area = 4 cm^2 is the same area = 6 cm^2

Add the areas to get the surface area of the cuboid:

6 cm$^2 + 6$ cm$^2 + 4$ cm$^2 + 4$ cm$^2 + 6$ cm$^2 + 6$ cm$^2 = 32$ cm^2

The surface area of the cuboid is 32 cm^2.

Exercise S4.4

1 Write the area of each net in square centimetres.

a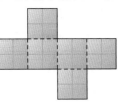

b

2 Find the surface area of each cuboid.

a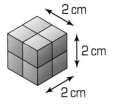
2 cm
2 cm
2 cm

b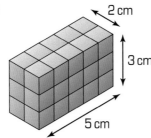
2 cm
3 cm
5 cm

c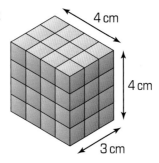
4 cm
4 cm
3 cm

3 Work out the volume and surface area of each cuboid.

a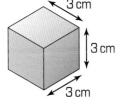
3 cm
3 cm
3 cm

b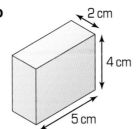
2 cm
4 cm
5 cm

> ► Volume is measured in centimetre cubes – cm³
>
> ► Area is measured in centimetre squares – cm²

4 The opposite faces of a dice always add up to 7.
Copy these nets and put the numbers 1 to 6 in the correct
places to make the nets of a dice.

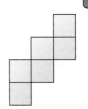

a

b

c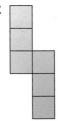

d

S4.5 Designing a box

This spread will show you how to:

▶▶ Construct nets of cuboids.

KEYWORDS
Cuboid   Net   Cube

Special chocolates come packed in small cubes.

Each cube measures
2 cm × 2 cm × 2 cm.

The cubes are sold in packs of 20.

To design the best box to hold the cubes, you need to think about:

1 The type of box you design – no gaps means no waste!

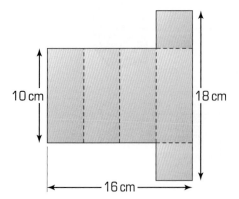

You can design more than one sort of box to hold 20 cubes.

2 The dimensions of the box.
2 × 2 cm = 4 cm
5 × 2 cm = 10 cm

Front elevation

4 cm

10 cm

Side elevation

4 cm

4 cm

Plan

4 cm

10 cm

3 The net of the box.

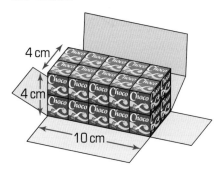

10 cm

18 cm

16 cm

Exercise S4.5

1 Drawing pins are sold in boxes like this one.
length = 5 cm
width = 3 cm
height = 2 cm

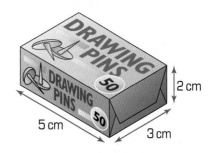

Pete joins 2 boxes together in different ways.
What are the lengths *a* and *b*?

2 Match boxes come in boxes like this.
length = 7 cm
width = 4.6 cm
height = 3 cm

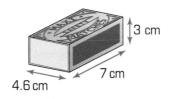

The boxes are packed 5 in a row.

a Use squared paper to draw the net of the box that the match boxes are wrapped in.

b What are the dimensions of the box?

This spread will show you how to:
▶▶ Construct nets of solid shapes.
▶▶ Visualise 3-D shapes from 2-D diagrams.

When you open out a box you can see its net.

You should know these common 3-D shapes.

Cube	Cuboid	Prism	Pyramid

All square faces | Rectangular faces | Cross-section the same throughout its length. | Comes together in a point.

The nets of these shapes look like this:

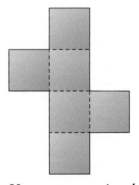 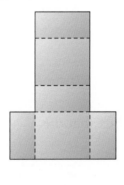 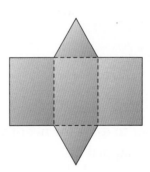 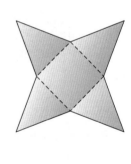

You name a prism by its cross-section:

 Triangular prism

 Hexagonal prism

You name a pyramid by its base:

 Square based pyramid

 Triangle-based pyramid

Exercise S4.6

1 These are the nets of 4 solid shapes.
What shape will each net make when it is folded?

a

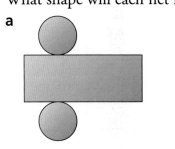

b

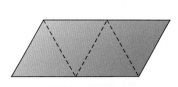

c

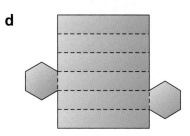

d

2 Using squared paper, copy and cut out these nets.
Fold the nets to make 3 solid shapes.

a

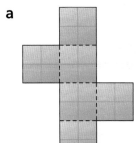

b

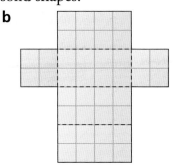

c

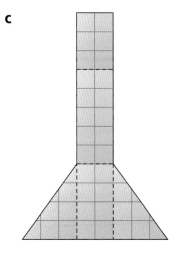

> You will have made a cube, a cuboid and a triangular prism.

3 Draw the net for this cuboid accurately on cm squared paper.

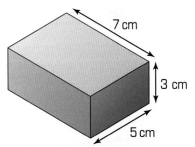

7 cm

3 cm

5 cm

You should know how to ...

1 Visualise 3-D shapes from 2-D diagrams.

Check out

1 Which of the nets fold to make this cuboid?

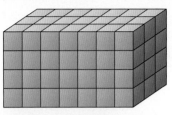

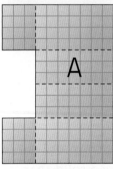

A

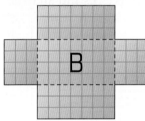

B

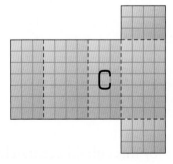

C

2 Calculate the surface area of a cuboid.

2 Calculate the surface area of the cuboid in question 1.

3 Calculate the volume of a cuboid.

3 Calculate the volume of the cuboid in question 1.

This unit will show you how to:

- ▶▶ Understand and use the probability scale.
- ▶▶ Find probabilities based on equally likely outcomes.
- ▶▶ Write probabilities as percentages.
- ▶▶ Recognise the equivalence of fractions, decimals and percentages.

- ▶▶ Recognise equivalent probabilities of outcomes happening.
- ▶▶ Reduce a fraction to its simplest form by cancelling.
- ▶▶ Identify all the possible outcomes of 2 events.
- ▶▶ Find and justify probabilities.

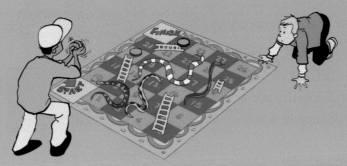

Probability will help you to understand games of chance.

Before you start

You should know how to ...

1 Use the language associated with probability to describe events.

Check in

1 There are 13 cards in this set.

Choose the word that best describes the chance of each event.

Use certain, likely, unlikely or impossible.

a Picking an ace.

b Picking a black card.

c Picking a card with a number on it.

d Picking a heart.

2 Use fraction notation.

2 What fraction of the cards in question 1 are:

a aces?

b picture cards?

c an even number?

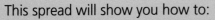

This spread will show you how to:

▶▶ Understand and use the probability scale from 0 to 1.
▶▶ Find probabilities based on equally likely outcomes.

KEYWORDS
Probability   Event
Fair outcome

▶ Probability is the chance or likelihood of an event occurring.

You can write probability as a fraction.

▶ Probability of an event happening = $\dfrac{\text{number of favourable outcomes}}{\text{total number of outcomes}}$

There is 1 ace in this set of 5 cards:
The chance of picking the ace is 1 chance in 5.
As a fraction, 1 chance in 5 $= \frac{1}{5}$.

You can show this probability on a probability scale.

There are 3 aces in this set of 5 cards:
The chance of picking an ace is now 3 chances
in 5.
As a fraction, 3 chances in 5 $= \frac{3}{5}$.

On a probability scale:

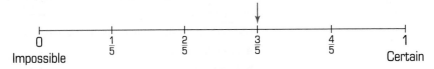

example

Here is a fair Treasure Wheel. It spins to give a prize.
As a fraction, what is the probability of Gold being selected?

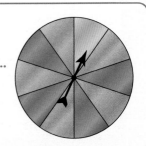

Gold has 1 chance in 10 of being selected.
As a fraction this is $\frac{1}{10}$.

Exercise D4.1

1 a Find the probability of picking a red cube from each bag.

 i ii iii iv v

b Copy this probability scale and mark on your answers.

0    $\frac{1}{6}$ $\frac{1}{3}$ $\frac{1}{2}$ $\frac{2}{3}$ $\frac{5}{6}$ 1

2 This fair spinner is marked with different numbers.

a Find the probability that the spinner lands on
   i 6.
   ii an even number.
b What is the probability of the spinner landing on a red section?

3 Emily has 5 dice.

She rolls each dice 60 times.
This table shows her results.

Only 2 of her dice are fair.
Using the table, write which dice are fair.
Give a reason for your answer.

	⚀	⚁	⚂	⚃	⚄	⚅
Dice 1	10	2	7	6	22	8
Dice 2	3	8	8	18	8	19
Dice 3	9	10	11	11	10	9
Dice 4	11	9	9	11	11	9
Dice 5	17	8	2	17	0	16

4 This is a set of 10 cards.

Write the probability of picking:
a an ace
b a card that is not an ace
Write your answers as a fraction.

5 Ali has an unfair dice.
The probability of throwing a 6 is $\frac{7}{10}$.
He rolls the dice 10 times.
How many times would he expect to get a 6?

This spread will show you how to:

▶▶ Find and justify probabilities based on equally likely outcomes.

▶▶ Recognise the equivalence between decimals and fractions.

There are 6 possible outcomes on this spinner: 1, 2, 3, 4, 5 or 6.

The probability of the spinner landing on a particular number is: 1 chance in 6 or $\frac{1}{6}$.

▶ The probability of an event $= \dfrac{\text{number of favourable outcomes}}{\text{total number of outcomes}}$.

There can be more than 1 favourable outcome.

The probability of the spinner landing on blue is $\frac{1+1}{6} = \frac{2}{6} = \frac{1}{3}$.

The probability of the spinner not landing on blue is the same as the probability of it landing on yellow, red, green or purple: $= \frac{1+1+1+1}{6} = \frac{4}{6} = \frac{2}{3}$.

▶ All probabilities add up to 1: $\frac{2}{6} + \frac{4}{6} = \frac{6}{6} = 1$

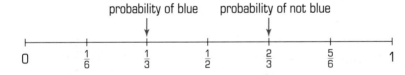

example

Inside this bag there are 10 counters.
3 of the counters are black. Find:

a the probability of picking a black counter.
b the probability of not picking a black counter.

Write your answers as decimals.

....

a The probability of picking a black counter is 3 chances in $10 = \frac{3}{10} = 0.3$.

b The probability of not picking a black counter is 7 chances in $10 = \frac{7}{10} = 0.7$.
Another way to find this probability is:
probability of not picking = 1 − probability of a black counter
$$= 1 - 0.3 = 0.7$$

Exercise D4.2

1 Here are 6 groups of counters.

i
ii
iii
iv
v
vi

Find, for each group:
a the probability of picking a red counter.
b the probability of not picking a red counter.
Write your answers as fractions and as decimals.
Use this probability scale to help you.

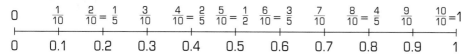

| 0 | $\frac{1}{10}$ | $\frac{2}{10}=\frac{1}{5}$ | $\frac{3}{10}$ | $\frac{4}{10}=\frac{2}{5}$ | $\frac{5}{10}=\frac{1}{2}$ | $\frac{6}{10}=\frac{3}{5}$ | $\frac{7}{10}$ | $\frac{8}{10}=\frac{4}{5}$ | $\frac{9}{10}$ | $\frac{10}{10}=1$ |
| 0 | 0.1 | 0.2 | 0.3 | 0.4 | 0.5 | 0.6 | 0.7 | 0.8 | 0.9 | 1 |

2 Here are 10 cards. The probability of picking a black card is 0.3.

a What is the probability of not picking a black card?
b Is the probability of picking a red card the same as picking a black card?
c What is the probability of picking a red card?

3 Here are 5 cards. The probability of picking a red card is $\frac{3}{5}$.
a What is the probability of picking a black card?
b Is the probability of picking a black card 0.2?
Explain your answer.

4 In each drawing the red counters are covered up and you can see all of the blue counters.
The probability of picking a blue counter is given.
Calculate the number of red counters for each drawing.

a

probability of blue = $\frac{1}{2}$

b

probability of blue = $\frac{1}{3}$

c

probability of blue = $\frac{1}{5}$

d

probability of blue = $\frac{1}{7}$

This spread will show you how to:

▶▶ Write probabilities as percentages.
▶▶ Recognise the equivalence of fractions, decimals and percentages.

▶ The probability of an event = $\dfrac{\text{number of favourable outcomes}}{\text{total number of outcomes}}$.

The probability of picking a red card from this set is an even chance. This is 1 chance out of 2 or $\frac{1}{2}$.

You can write probabilities as:

Fractions,   decimals   or percentages.
$\frac{1}{2}$ ⟶   0.5 ⟶   50%

Even means equal.

chance of picking a red card
↓

0%   50%   100%
├──────────────────────┼──────────────────────┤
0                     $\frac{1}{2}$ 1

▶ A percentage is a fraction out of 100.
$\frac{1}{2} = \frac{50}{100} = 50\%$

example

In this set there are 10 cards.
Find:

a the probability of picking a black card.
b the probability of picking a red card.

....

a There are 7 black cards.
The chance of picking a black card is $\frac{7}{10} = \frac{70}{100} = 70\%$.

b There are 3 red cards.
The chance of picking a red card is $\frac{3}{10} = \frac{30}{100} = 30\%$.

chance of picking a red card   chance of black card
↓   ↓

0%   10%   20%   30%   40%   50%   60%   70%   80%   90%   100%
├─────┼─────┼─────┼─────┼─────┼─────┼─────┼─────┼─────┼─────┤
0    $\frac{1}{10}$ $\frac{2}{10}$ $\frac{3}{10}$ $\frac{4}{10}$ $\frac{5}{10}$ $\frac{6}{10}$ $\frac{7}{10}$ $\frac{8}{10}$ $\frac{9}{10}$ $\frac{10}{10}$

Exercise D4.3

1 **a** Write the probabilities of picking a red card from each of these sets of cards.
   b What are the probabilities of not picking a red card from each set?

Write your answers as percentages.

i    **ii**    **iii**    **iv**    **v**

2 Here are 4 bags. Which bag gives you a 25% chance of picking a black bead?

a   **b**   **c**   **d**

3 List all of these outcomes that have a 50% probability of happening.
   a Flipping a coin and getting a 'head'.
   b Rolling a dice and getting a 6.

   c Traffic lights being on green.
   d This spinner landing on blue.

4 **a** What is the probability of this spinner landing on blue?
   b What is the probability of this spinner not landing on blue?
   c What is the probability of this spinner not landing on blue or red?
   Write your answers as percentages.

5 What is the percentage probability of each spinner landing on:
   a white   **b** orange   **c** blue   **d** green
   i   **ii**   **iii**

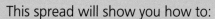

This spread will show you how to:

▶▶ Recognise equivalent probabilities of outcomes happening.

▶▶ Reduce a fraction to its simplest form by cancelling.

KEYWORDS

Equivalent

p(outcome)

Simplest form

Shamim has 4 bags of counters.

She says there is an equal probability of picking a blue counter from each bag.

p(blue) means the probability of picking blue.

p(blue) = $\frac{1}{2}$ = 50%   p(blue) = $\frac{2}{4}$ = $\frac{1}{2}$ = 50%   p(blue) = $\frac{3}{6}$ = $\frac{1}{2}$ = 50%   p(blue) = $\frac{5}{10}$ = $\frac{1}{2}$ = 50%

This means that for every blue counter there is 1 yellow counter.

Leo has another bag.
He writes: p(blue) = $\frac{3}{12}$

The 12 counters can be divided into groups of 4.

There is 1 chance in 4, of picking out a blue counter.
So, in its simplest form, he can write p(blue) = $\frac{1}{4}$.

▶ To find the probability in its simplest form, check to see if there is a number that will divide into the numerator and the denominator.

example

Write these probabilities in their simplest form:

a $\dfrac{3}{12}$

b $\dfrac{8}{12}$

a 3 will divide into the numerator and denominator.

$$\frac{3 \div 3}{12 \div 3} = \frac{1}{4}$$

b 4 will divide into the numerator and the denominator.

$$\frac{8 \div 4}{12 \div 4} = \frac{2}{3}$$

Exercise D4.4

1 There are 12 tiles in this bag.

  a The probability of picking a blue tile is $\frac{3}{12}$.
Write this probability in its simplest form.

  b What is the probability of picking a green tile?
Write your answer in its simplest form.

2 There are 6 faces on a dice. 1, 2, 3, 4, 5 and 6.
Write the probability that the dice will land on an even
number as:

  a a fraction in its simplest form.

  b a percentage.

3 Class 9B are playing Bingo. Samira has this card:

  a How many even numbers are there on her card?

  b Does she want odd or even numbers to be called out?

  c What would the probability be of picking an even
number at random from her card?
Write your answer in its simplest form.

  d What is the probability of picking a number from her
card that has the digit 7 in it?
Write your answer

    i in its simplest form

    ii as a percentage.

4 There are 9 cards here.

The chance of picking a black card at random is $\frac{2}{3}$.
How many black cards are there?

This spread will show you how to:

▶▶ Identify all the possible outcomes of 2 events.

KEYWORDS
Combination
Table

You can list all the possible outcomes of 2 events in simple cases.

The Year 9 Girls' Hockey squad are choosing colours for their sports kit. They can choose from:

Blue shirt   Red shirt   Blue skirt   Orange skirt

The events are choosing a shirt and choosing a skirt.

They draw the different possible combinations and put them in a table.

Skirts \ Shirts	Blue	Red
Blue	Blue Blue	Red Blue
Orange	Blue Orange	Red Orange

The table shows that there are 4 different combinations to choose from.

They add another colour of skirt to the table.

Skirts \ Shirts	Blue	Red
Blue	Blue Blue	Red Blue
Orange	Blue Orange	Red Orange
White	Blue White	Red White

The table shows that there are now 6 different kit combinations.

Exercise D4.5

1 a Copy and complete the table to list all of the possible combinations of flipping 2 coins.
The table has been started for you.

	1st coin	
2nd coin	**Heads**	**Tails**
Heads		Tails Heads
Tails		

b How many combinations are there altogether?

2 Here are all Mr Ross's shirts and ties.

a Copy and complete the table to show all the different combinations he could choose.

	Shirt			
Tie	**Stripe**	**Yellow**	**Blue**	**White**
Gold		Yellow Gold		
Blue Stripe				White Blue Stripe

b How many different combinations are there altogether?

3 Most Year 9 students will be able to choose their GCSE options before their summer holidays.
Here are 2 option groups that Henry Compton School offers.

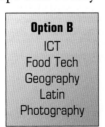

Option A
French
Art
History

Option B
ICT
Food Tech
Geography
Latin
Photography

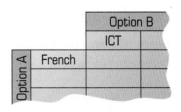

		Option B
		ICT
Option A	French	

The Year 9 options table has been started for you.

a How many columns will you need for Option B?
b How many rows will you need for Option A?
c Copy and complete the table for both option groups.
d How many different combinations can Henry Compton students choose from?

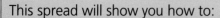

This spread will show you how to:

▶▶ Identify all the possible outcomes of 2 events.
▶▶ Find and justify probabilities.

KEYWORDS
Event
Outcome

You can use a table to help you list all the possible outcomes of 2 events.

The sides of these 2 spinners are numbered.

The scores on the spinners are added together and recorded in this probability table.

Triangular spinner

+	1	2	3
1	1 + 1 = 2	1 + 2 = 3	4
2	3	4	5
3	4	5	6
4	5	6	7

(Square spinner — labelled along left side)

You can use the table to find the probability of different scores or outcomes.

There are 12 outcomes shown in the table.

There is 1 score of 2 in the table and there are 12 outcomes.
▶ The probability of scoring 2 is $\frac{1}{12}$.

There are 2 scores of 3 out of the 12 outcomes in the table.
▶ The probability of scoring 3 is $\frac{2}{12}$ or $\frac{1}{6}$.

There are 3 scores of 5 out of the 12 outcomes in the table.
▶ The probability of scoring 5 is $\frac{3}{12}$ or $\frac{1}{4}$.

There are 6 even scores out of the 12 outcomes in the table.
▶ The probability of an even score is $\frac{6}{12}$ or $\frac{1}{2}$.

Use fractions to write the probabilities.

▶ The probability of an odd score is 1 − p (even score).
p(odd) = $1 - \frac{1}{2} = \frac{1}{2}$.

Exercise D4.6

1 **a** Copy and complete the table for picking 2 out of 4 counters. (You put the counter back after picking it) The outcomes are black and white, use **b** and **w**.

b How many outcomes are there altogether?

c Use the table to find the probability of an outcome of 2 blacks.

d Find the probability of 1 black and 1 white?

e What is the probability of picking at least 1 white?

First counter

Second counter		Black	White
	Black	b and b	
	White		

2 The outcomes recorded in this table show the different ways that these spinners can land.

a How many outcomes will there be altogether in the table? You can copy and complete the table to help you.

First spinner

Second spinner		Yellow	Blue	Green	Red
	Blue	Yellow Blue		Green Blue	
	Red		Blue Red		Red Red
	Green			Green Green	

b What is the probability of the 2 spinners landing on a red?

3 Pete rolls 2 dice and adds their scores. The table shows the outcomes.

a How many outcomes are there altogether?

b Explain how you could calculate your answer to **a**.

c Which score is the most frequent?

d What is the probability of scoring 7?

e Is it possible to score 13?

f Which 2 scores both have a probability of $\frac{1}{12}$?

First dice

Second dice	+	1	2	3	4	5	6
	1	2		4	5		7
	2		4				
	3						9
	4		6				
	5			8		10	
	6			10			

You should know how to ...

1 Find probabilities based on equally likely outcomes.

2 Reduce a fraction to its simplest form by cancelling.

3 Understand and use the probability scale from 0 to 1.

Check out

1 Find the probability of picking a red counter from each of these bags.

a

b

c

d

2 Write each of the probabilities in question 1 in their simplest form.

$$0 \qquad \frac{1}{6} \qquad \frac{1}{3} \qquad \frac{1}{2} \qquad \frac{2}{3} \qquad \frac{5}{6} \qquad 1$$

3 Mark each of the probabilities in question 1 on a copy of this probability scale.

This unit will show you how to:

▶▶ Solve problems and investigate in a range of contexts.

▶▶ Identify the necessary information to solve a problem.

▶▶ Use two-way tables.

▶▶ Solve a problem by breaking it down into smaller steps.

▶▶ Represent problems and interpret solutions in algebraic and graphical form.

▶▶ Compare and evaluate solutions.

You can use models to investigate problems.

Before you start

You should know how to ...

1 Continue number patterns.

2 Use letter symbols.

3 Plot graphs of simple linear functions.

Check in

1 Write the next 2 terms in each sequence:

    a 3, 6, 9, __, __   **b** 7, 11, 15, __, __

2 If $x = 3$ and $y = 4$, work out

    a $x + y$ **b** $3x$ **c** $2x + 4y$

3 a Copy and complete this table of values for the line $y = x + 3$.

x	0	1	2	3	4
+3	+3	+3	+3	+3	+3
y	3		5		

    b Copy these axes and plot the line.

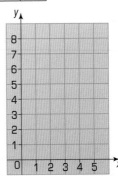

This spread will show you how to:
▶▶ Solve problems and investigate in a range of contexts.

In this unit you will complete an investigation similar to your Maths coursework at GCSE.

As you work through the investigation you need to keep notes and organise your work.

When you begin your investigation you need to:

▶ make sure you understand the task.
▶ work systematically and record your results carefully.
▶ look for patterns and rules, and try to explain how the pattern works.
▶ use tables, graphs and charts to display your results.
▶ check your results for errors.

To complete this investigation you will need to:

▶ construct a table of results
▶ draw graphs, charts and tables
▶ make accurate calculations
▶ see patterns in numbers
▶ work neatly and carefully.

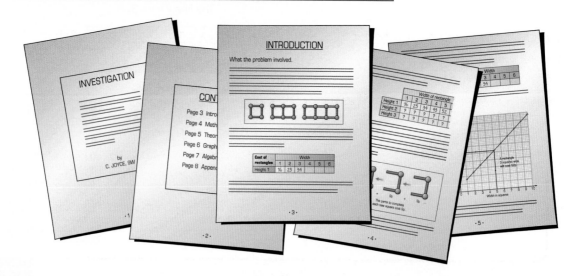

Exercise B1.1

1 Describe these number patterns in your own words.

    a 2, 5, 8, 11, ___, ___

    b 88, 93, 98, 103, ___, ___

    c 41, 35, 29, 23, ___, ___

    d 1, 2, 4, 7, 11, ___, ___

2 What are the next 2 numbers in each pattern in question 1?

3 Work out the cost of:

    a 5 nuts, 5 washers and 5 bolts?

    b 8 nuts, 7 washers and 4 bolts?

    c 11 nuts, 9 washers and 6 bolts?

nut = 2p   washer = 1p   bolt = 4p

4 Rory is untidy in his work and careless with his calculations.
Redraw the table and bar chart neatly, and correct his errors.

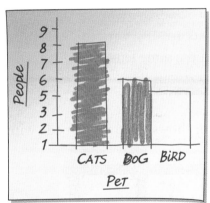

favourite pets	tally	frequency
CATS	⊬⊦⊦ III	8
DOG	III	4
BIRD	⊬⊦	5

Survey of favourite pets

5 During your investigation you will need this table to record your results.
Carefully draw this table.
Draw all the lines with a pencil and ruler.

	Width of rectangle									
	1	2	3	4	5	6	7	8	9	10
Height 1										
Height 2										
Height 3										

Understanding the investigation

This spread will show you how to:

▶▶ Solve problems and investigate in a range of contexts.
▶▶ Identify the necessary information to solve a problem.

It is now time for you to prepare for your investigation.

The title for the investigation is:

My investigation into the link between the cost and the size of rectangles constructed from a model kit.

A model construction kit is made from **rods** that lock together with **connectors**.

Each rod costs 1p.
(Rods are all the same length)

Each connector costs 3p.

This diagram shows a rectangle made with the kit.

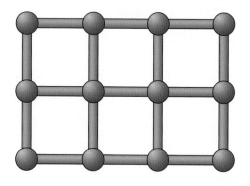

This rectangle has an area of 6 square units.

To make this rectangle 12 connectors and 17 rods were used.

This rectangle would cost:

12 connectors at 3p = 36p
17 rods at 1p = 17p
Total = 53p

Investigate:

▶ the largest rectangle you can make for a total cost of £1 or less.

▶ the cost of other rectangles made from the kit.

Exercise B1.2

This exercise will help you structure and organise your investigation.

Start by trying a few examples.
Make sure you understand how the investigation works.

1 Work out the cost of making these rectangles with the rods
and connectors.
Show your working out.

 a 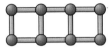 **b** 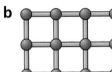 **c**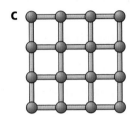

Use simple drawings
to represent the rods
and connectors.

Get some general ideas about how the results change.
For example, the area of 'b' is twice as big as the area of 'a'.
Does it cost twice as much?

2 Jackie says:

I'm going to make a rectangle with an area of 12 squares.
Does the cost change if I make the rectangle a different way?

All of these rectangles have an area of 12 square units.
Work out the cost of each one.

a 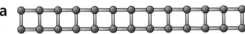 **b** **c**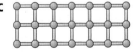

Use your results to answer Jackie's question.

Once you understand the problem, go back to the instructions.

The first part of the investigation asked you to find the biggest
rectangle you can make for £1 or less.

3 You can make a rectangle with an area of 12 squares units for less than £1.
Now check to see if you can make a bigger rectangle for less than £1.

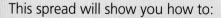
This spread will show you how to:

▶▶ Identify the necessary information to solve a problem.
▶▶ Use 2-way tables.
▶▶ Solve a problem by breaking it down into smaller steps.

KEYWORDS

Systematic   2-way table
Diagram   Difference

You start an investigation by trying lots of examples.
You then need to work systematically and organise your results.

Break the problems into steps

There are 2 things you can change about a rectangle – its width and its height.
If you keep 1 the same you can see what is going on more clearly.

  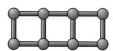

The height is the same, and the width increases by 1 square each time.
You can work out how much the cost increases each time the width increases by 1.

▶ To work systematically, change just 1 thing at a time.

Record your results

You can record the cost of each rectangle in a table like this:

Cost of rectangles	Width					
	1	2	3	4	5	6
Height 1	16	25	34			

Remember:
Connectors cost 3p
Rods cost 1p

You can then increase the height of the rectangle to 2 squares.

  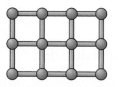

You can enter your results in a 2-way table like this:

Cost of rectangles	Width					
	1	2	3	4	5	6
Height 1						
Height 2						

▶ Putting the results in a table makes it easier to spot patterns.

Exercise B1.3

1 Here are the first 3 rectangles that are 1 square high.
The cost of these rectangles is recorded in the table.

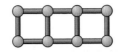

			Width of rectangle							
	1	2	3	4	5	6	7	8	9	10
Height 1	16	25	34							

Use your table from Exercise B1.1.
Fill in the cost of the other rectangles 1 square high.
(Draw some of the rectangles to help find the result.)

Remember:
Connectors cost 3p
Rods cost 1p

2 These rectangles are 2 squares high.

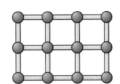

			Width of rectangle							
	1	2	3	4	5	6	7	8	9	10
Height 1	16	25	34							
Height 2										

On your copy of the table, fill in as many results as you
can for rectangles of 2 squares height.

3 Now calculate costs for rectangles 3 squares high.

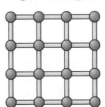

			Width of rectangle							
	1	2	3	4	5	6	7	8	9	10
Height 1	16	25	34							
Height 2										
Height 3										

Hint: Look at the difference between each result.

▶ Look along each row and see if you can find the number pattern.
▶ Use this pattern to work out the 11th and 12th result for each row.

This spread will show you how to:

▶▶ Represent problems and interpret solutions in algebraic form.

KEYWORDS
Algebra   Formula
Systematic

You can explain why the number patterns work, and describe them in words.

These rectangles are 1 square high:

  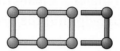

To add another square, you use 3 rods and 2 connectors.
3 rods cost 3p and 2 connectors cost 6p.
The total cost of adding a square is 9p.

In this table the numbers in the row for height 1 go up by 9 each time.

Cost of rectangles	Width					
	1	2	3	4	5	6
Height 1	16	25	34	43		

+9   +9   +9

You should be able to describe rules and patterns using algebra.

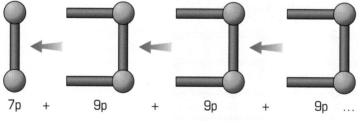

7p   +   9p   +   9p   +   9p   ...

The first part of the rectangle pattern costs 7p.

The parts to complete each new square cost 9p.

This pattern can be written as an algebraic formula:

The cost of any rectangle 1 square high = 7 + 9 times the width of the rectangle.

▶ $c = 7 + 9w$

Exercise B1.4

1 Use the formula $c = 7 + 9c$ to calculate the cost of these 1 square high rectangles:

a 5 squares wide **b** 11 squares wide **c** 15 squares wide

2 These rectangles are 2 squares high.

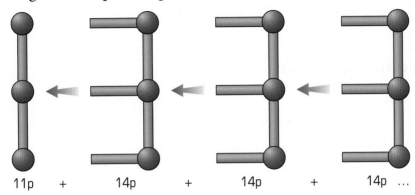

11p + 14p + 14p + 14p ...

The first part of the rectangle pattern costs 11p.

The parts to make the rectangles 1 square wider cost 14p.

Work out the algebraic formula to calculate the cost of any rectangle 2 squares high.

3 This flow chart shows the steps you need to take to describe and explain the number patterns in your table of results.

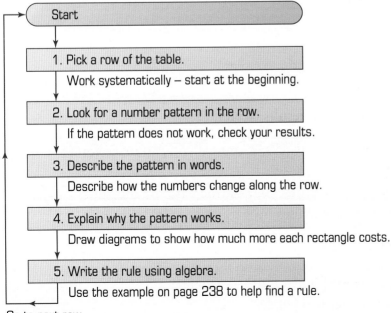

Start

1. Pick a row of the table.
   Work systematically – start at the beginning.

2. Look for a number pattern in the row.
   If the pattern does not work, check your results.

3. Describe the pattern in words.
   Describe how the numbers change along the row.

4. Explain why the pattern works.
   Draw diagrams to show how much more each rectangle costs.

5. Write the rule using algebra.
   Use the example on page 238 to help find a rule.

Go to next row

Explain the number patterns in your table of results by working through the steps in this chart.

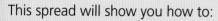

This spread will show you how to:

▶▶ Represent problems and interpret solutions in graphical form.

KEYWORDS

Graph
Trend

A graph is a good way to describe your results as it can show trends.

▶ A trend is an overall description of the graph.

Here is the table of results for rectangles 1 square high.

	Width of rectangle									
	1	2	3	4	5	6	7	8	9	10
Height 1	16	25	34	43	52	61	70	79	88	97

You get a straight line when you plot these on a graph.

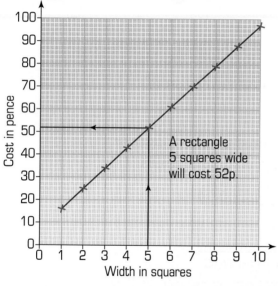

A rectangle
5 squares wide
will cost 52p

The graph makes some features of the results clearer:

▶ For rectangles 1 square high, the biggest rectangle you can make for £1 or less is 10 squares wide.
▶ The line is straight, which shows that the cost increases by the same amount each time the width increases by 1 square.

You need to read the graph carefully:

▶ The horizontal axis shows the width of the rectangle
▶ The vertical axis shows the cost in pence.
▶ It is not easy to read results from a graph. You must include a table of results and a graph in your investigation.

Exercise B1.5

1 Use the data from your table of results to draw a graph for:

a the first 5 results for rectangles 1 square high.

b the first 5 results for rectangles 2 squares high.

c the first 5 results for rectangles 3 squares high.

Copy these axes to help you.

	Width of rectangle				
	1	2	3	4	5
Height 1	16	25	34	43	52
Height 2	?	?	?	?	?
Height 3	?	?	?	?	?

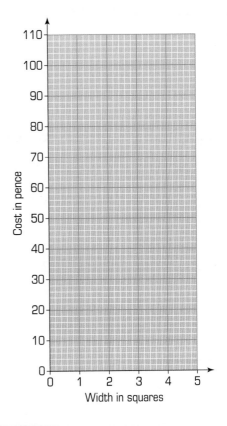

Remember:

▶ Plot the width of the rectangles on the horizontal axis

▶ Plot the cost of each rectangle on the vertical axis.

▶ Choose the scales for each axis carefully so that you can fit your grid onto the page.

▶ Give your graph a title and label it carefully.

Your graph will give you an opportunity to check your results. The points you plot should make a straight line.

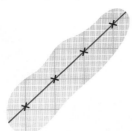

Your line should look like this.

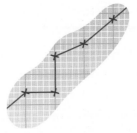

If it looks like this, check your results!

This spread will show you how to:
▶▶ Compare and evaluate solutions.

KEYWORDS
Systematic   Predict
Conclusion

These 3 steps are all you need to complete your investigation.
You have already worked through the first 2 steps.

1 Work systematically to generate results

▶ Do not change everything at once.
Change 1 thing at a time so that you can see the effects.

▶ Record and present your results in an organised way such as a table.

▶ Check your results carefully.
Do not just continue a number pattern without checking it is correct.

2 Describe and justify patterns and rules

▶ Describe patterns in your results using words, algebra and graphs.

▶ Explain why your rules work, by showing the connection between the number patterns and the situation you are investigating.

▶ Use your rule to predict and check further results.

The third step should help you to produce a report about your findings:

3 Communicate your results clearly and effectively

▶ Use appropriate tables, graphs, diagrams and algebra to represent your findings.

▶ Use headings to make your report easy to follow.

▶ Make conclusions based on the question asked.

▶ Justify any conclusions by referring to your findings.

▶ You do not have to include all of your working in the main part of your report, but do give some examples of how you worked through problems.

Exercise B1.6

Your finished investigation will probably include these sections:

1 Title page

2 Contents page

3 Introduction

Explain what the investigation is about.

4 Results

Explain how you found and checked your results.
Show the results that you need using tables and graphs.
You only need to include a few examples to show what you did.

Describe and explain the patterns in your results.
Use words and algebra to describe the patterns in your results.
It is important to try to explain why the rules work.

5 Conclusions

Look back at the original questions and give your answers to them clearly.
In this investigation there was 1 question with 1 answer:

▸ Find the largest rectangle you can make for £1 or less,
 and a second question that you could answer in lots of ways,
▸ Find the cost of other rectangles made from the kit.

6 Additional information

Include any working that you want
to show.

> It is a good idea to have page numbers on your report, and to label every chart and diagram.
>
> This makes it easier to refer to other parts of your report – 'See Diagram 7 on page 5'.

You should know how to ...

1 Identify the necessary information to solve a problem.

2 Represent problems and interpret solutions in algebraic and graphical form.

Check out

1 Write a set of **Hints and Tips** that you would give to somebody starting on a mathematical investigation.

You could include advice about how to:
▶ Organise the work
▶ Set out the results
▶ Check the results
▶ Find rules
▶ Report the findings of the investigation.

2 In your investigation, you had the opportunity to represent your results in various forms:
▶ Table of results
▶ Graphs to represent your results
▶ Rules in words or using algebra.

Explain the advantages and disadvantages of each of these ways of presenting your results. You should describe how easy each method is to carry out, and how clearly it describes what is going on.

2-D shape
S1.4

A 2-D shape is a flat shape.

2-way table
B1.3

A 2-way table is used to show the result when you change 2 variables, for example the length and width of a rectangle.

		Width of rectangle		
		1	2	3
Height of rectangle	1	1	2	3
	2	2	4	6
	3	3	6	9

3-D shape
S1.9, S4.2

A 3-D shape is a solid.

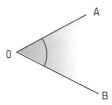

accurate
N2.6

An accurate answer is calculated using exact values.

add, addition
A4.3

Addition is the sum of two numbers or quantities.

algebra
B1.4

In algebra symbols or letters are used to represent numbers.

angle: acute, obtuse, right, reflex
S1.2

An angle is formed when two straight lines cross or meet each other at a point. The size of an angle is measured in degrees (°).

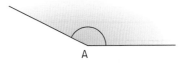

An acute angle is less than 90°.

An obtuse angle is more than 90° but less than 180°.

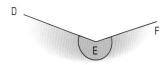

A right-angle is a quarter of a turn, or 90°.

A reflex angle is more than 180° but less than 360°.

angles at a point
S1.2, S3.1, S4.1

Angles at a point add up to 360°.

$$a + b + c = 360°$$

angles in a quadrilateral
S1.5, S4.1

Angles in a quadrilateral add up to 360°.

$$a + b + c + d = 360°$$

angles in a triangle
S1.3, S1.5, S4.1

Angles in a triangle add up to 180°.

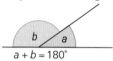

$$a + b + c = 180°$$

angles on a straight line
S1.2, S1.3, S3.1, S4.1

Angles on a straight line add up to 180°.

$$a + b = 180°$$

anticlockwise
S3.1

Anticlockwise movement is the opposite way to the hands of a clock.

apex
S1.9

The highest point of a shape is the apex.

approximate,
approximately (≈)
S2.6, N2.6

An approximate value is close to the actual value of a number or measure.

area: square millimetre,
square centimetre,
square metre,
square kilometre
A3.5, S2.2, S2.3, P1.5

The area of a surface is a measure of its size.
Area is measured in units squared, for example, mm^2, cm^2, m^2, km^2.

average
D1.2

An average is used to represent a set of values.

axis, axes
S2.1

An axis is one of the lines used to locate a point on a grid using coordinates.

balance
P1.3

An equation balances when the value is the same on both sides of the equals sign.

bar chart
D1.4, D3.4

A bar chart is a diagram that uses rectangles of equal width to display data. The frequency is given by the height of the rectangle.

base (of a shape)
S1.9

The lower horizontal edge of a flat shape is usually called the base. The base of a solid is the face that sits on the ground.

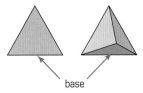

base

bearing
S3.1

A bearing is measured clockwise from North.
The bearing of A from B is 045°.

brackets
A5.1

Operations in brackets should be done first.

cancel
N1.1

When you cancel a fraction, you divide the numerator and the denominator by the same number. When you cancel a ratio, you divide both parts of the ratio by the same number.

capacity: millilitre, litre
S2.6

Capacity is the amount of liquid a container will hold.
It is measured in litres and millilitres.
1 litre = 1000 millilitres

centre of rotation
S3.2

The centre of rotation is the point about which a shape rotates.

certain
D2.3

An event which is certain will definitely happen.

chance
D2.3

Chance is the probability of something happening.

chunk, chunking
N2.7

Chunking is a method for dividing. You subtract chunks of the number you are dividing by.
For example: To work out 900 ÷ 30, you can subtract chunks of 30.
A chunk of ten 30's is 300.
900 − 300 = 600 ... 10 × 30
600 − 300 = 300 ... another 10 × 30
300 − 300 = 0 ... another 10 × 30
So 900 ÷ 30 = 30

Glossary

class
D2.1, D2.2

To sort a large amount of data you can group the data into classes.

clockwise
S3.1

Clockwise movement is the same way as the hands of a clock.

collect
A3.1

Collect means 'gather together'. You can collect like terms to simplify an expression. For example $x + x = 2x$.

combination
D4.5

The different ways of choosing or getting 2 or more things are the combinations.
For example, when you toss 2 coins the possible combinations are 2 heads, a head on the 1st coin and a tail on the 2nd, a tail on the 1st coin and a head on the 2nd and 2 tails.

comparative bar chart
D1.4

A comparative bar chart is a bar chart with a group of bars for each category. It is useful for making comparisons within categories.

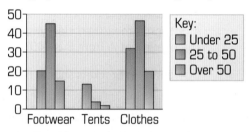

compare
D3.6

Compare means to look at similar and different aspects of things.

compass
S3.1

A compass is used to find directions. The needle always points to North.

compensate, compensation
N2.4, N2.5

Compensation makes some calculations easier, for example, to find 4×99 you can work out 4×100 and compensate by subtracting 4 from the answer.

conclusion
B1.6

A conclusion is a decision you reach after series of steps.

congruent
S1.1, S4.1

Congruent shapes are exactly the same shape and size.
They are identical.

convert
N2.4

Convert means to change.

coordinates
A2.2, S2.1, A4.5, A4.6,
A4.7, A4.8

Coordinates are the numbers that make up a coordinate pair.
They describe the position of a point on a grid.

cross-section
S4.6

A cross-section is what you get when you cut through a solid.

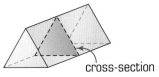

cross-section

cube
S2.4, S4.5, S4.6

A cube is a 3-D square. All the sides are the same length.

cuboid
S2.4, S2.5, S4.3, S4.4,
S4.5, S4.6

A cuboid is a 3-D rectangle.

data
A2.3, D1.1, D1.6

Data are pieces of information.

decimals, decimal fraction
N1.5, N2.3

A decimal fraction, or decimal, shows part of a whole represented as
tenths, hundredths, thousandths and so on.
For example, 0.65 and 0.3 are decimal fractions.

decimal point
N2.2

A decimal point separates the whole number part of a number from
the decimal part.

degree (°)
S1.2

A degree is a measure of turn. There are 360° in a full turn.

denominator
N1.1, N1.2, N1.3, N1.4

The denominator is the bottom number in a fraction.
It shows how many parts the whole has been divided into.

 $\frac{1}{2}$ ← denominator

diagram
B1.3

A diagram is a line drawing that illustrates a situation.

difference
B1.3

You find the difference between two amounts by subtracting one
from the other.

digit
N2.2

A digit is any of the numbers 0, 1, 2, 3, 4, 5, 6, 7, 8, 9.

Glossary

dimensions
S1.9, S2.4, S4.3

The dimensions of an object are its measurements.

direction
S3.2

A direction is the way you go. For example, North or anticlockwise.

discrete data
D3.4

Discrete data are data that can be counted, for example, the shoe size of Year 9 students.

distance
A2.3

The distance between two points is the length of the line that joins them.

divide, division
NA1.4, N1.8

Divide (÷) means share equally.
$6 \div 2 = 3$

edge
S1.9

An edge is a line along which two faces of a solid or shape meet.

edge

elevation
S4.2

An elevation is an accurate drawing of the side or front of a solid.

enlarge, enlargement
S3.5

An enlargement is a transformation that multiples the length of all the sides of a shape by the same scale factor.

equal, equals (=)
P1.3

Equal means having exactly the same value or size.

equal (sides, angles)
S1.3

Equal sides are the same length. Equal angles are the same size.

equally likely
D4.2

Events are equally likely if they have the same probability.

equation
A3.3, A4.4, A4.6, A5.4

An equation is a statement linking two expressions that have the same value.

equivalent, equivalence
N1.1, N1.3, N1.5, D4.4

Equivalent fractions have the same value; equivalent probabilities are the same.

estimate
P1.6

An estimate is an approximate answer.

evaluate
A5.2, A5.3

You can evaluate an expression when you have values for all the letters or symbols. You replace the letters with the numbers and work out the value of the expression.

even chance
D4.3

Even chance means that either choice is equally likely.

event
D2.3, D2.4, D4.1, D4.6

An event is an activity, or the result of an activity.
For example, tossing a coin.

experiment
D2.4

An experiment is a test or investigation to gather evidence for or
against a suggestion. In probability, an experiment is a series of trials.

experimental probability
D2.4

Experimental probability is calculated on the basis of the results of an
experiment.

$$\text{Experimental probability of an event} = \frac{\text{number of successful trials}}{\text{total number of trials}}.$$

expression
A3.1, A3.2, A5.2, A5.3

An expression is a collection of numbers and symbols linked by
operations but not including an equals sign.

exterior angle
S1.3

An exterior angle is made by extending one side of shape.

face
S1.9, S4.4

A face is a flat surface of a solid.

face

factor
N1.7, N1.9, N2.6, N2.7, A4.1,
A5.1

A factor is a number that divides exactly into another number.
For example, 3 and 7 are factors of 21.

factorise
A5.1

When you factorise a number you break it down into 2 or more
factors that multiply together to give the original number.
For example, you can factorise 20 as 2 × 10.

fair
D4.1

A fair chance is one that is equally likely; a fair dice or spinner is one
for which each possible outcome is equally likely.

formula, formulas
A1.2, A5.3, A5.6, B1.4

A formula is used to calculate a quantity.

fraction
N1.1

A fraction is a way of describing a part of a whole.
For example, $\frac{2}{5}$ of this shape is shaded.

Glossary

frequency
D1.3

Frequency is the number of times something occurs.

frequency diagram
D3.5

A frequency diagram uses bars to display grouped data.
The height of each bar gives the frequency of the group, and there is no space between the bars.

frequency table
D1.3, D3.1

A frequency table is a neat way of listing the frequency of different events.

Pet	Frequency
Dog	9
Cat	3

full turn
S1.2

A full turn is 360°.

function machine
A3.4

A function machine links an input to an output by doing a function.

Input	Operation	Output
10	× 3	30

graph
A5.6, B1.5

A graph shows the link between different data.

greater than (>)
N1.3

Greater than means bigger than. For example 4 is greater than 3, or $4 > 3$

grid
P1.6

A grid is a square pattern. You can use a grid to plot coordinate points. You can also use a grid to multiply two numbers.

grouped data
D2.1, P1.2

Grouped data are data that have been sorted into groups and then values in each group added up.

horizontal
A4.9

Horizontal means flat and level with the ground.

hundreds, tens, units, tenths, hundredths, thousandths
N2.1

Hundred = 100

Ten = 10

Unit = 1

Tenth = 0.1 or $\frac{1}{10}$

Hundredth = 0.01 or $\frac{1}{100}$

Thousandth = 0.001 or $\frac{1}{1000}$

hypothesis
D3.1

A hypothesis is what you can say may happen.
You test a hypothesis by collecting data.

image
S3.2, S3.3

When a shape is reflected, translated, rotated or enlarged, the new shape is called the image.

imperial: mile, pint, gallon
S2.6

The imperial system is an older way of measuring which some people still use.

impossible
D2.3

An event is impossible if it definitely cannot happen.

input
A3.4

Input is data put into a machine or process.

interior angle
S1.3

An interior angle is inside a shape, between 2 adjacent sides.

interpret
D1.1

You interpret data whenever you make sense of it.

intersect, intersection
S1.1, S1.7

Two lines intersect at the point where they cross. This is the intersection of the lines.

interval
D2.1, D2.2

An interval is the size of a class or group in a frequency table.

inverse, inverse operation
A3.3, A3.4, A5.4, A5.5

An inverse operation undoes the original operation.
For example, multiplication is the inverse of division.

investigate, investigation
B1.1, B1.2

When you investigate something, you find out more about it.

jottings
P1.4, P1.6

Jottings are rough notes.

key
P1.2, D3.3

You use a key to explain a scale or colour coding used in a diagram.

length: millimetre, centimetre, metre, kilometre; mile, foot, inch
S2.2

Length is a measure of distance. It is often used to describe one dimension of a shape.
  One kilometre = 1000 metres
      One metre = 100 centimetres
One centimetre = 10 millimetres

Glossary

less than (<)
N1.3

Less than means smaller than.
For example, 3 is less than 4, or $3 < 4$.

like terms
A3.1

Like terms use the same letter and can be collected together. For example, $2a$ and $6a$ are like terms. $2a + 6a = 8a$.

likelihood
D2.3, D4.1

Likelihood is the probability of an event happening.

likely
D2.3

An event is likely if it will happen more often than not.

line graph
D1.5, D3.4

A line graph shows how something changes over a certain time.

line of symmetry
S3.4

You can fold a 2-D shape along a line of symmetry so that one half of the shape fits exactly on the other half.
See also mirror line.

LOGO
S1.8

Software used to draw shapes on a computer.

lowest common multiple (LCM)
A4.1

The lowest common multiple is the smallest multiple shared by 2 or more numbers.
For example, the lowest common multiple of 4 and 6 is 12.

mass: gram, kilogram
S2.6

The mass of an object is how heavy it is. It is measured in kilograms or grams.

mean
D1.2, P1.1, D3.2

The mean is an average value found by adding all the values and dividing by the number of values.

median
D1.2, P1.1, D3.2, D3.3

The median is an average which is the middle value when the data is arranged in size order.

1 2 3 ⑥ 9 12 13

The median of these numbers is 6.

metric
S2.6

The metric system is a way of measuring. There are units for measuring length, mass and capacity.

midpoint
S1.6

The midpoint of a line is halfway between the 2 endpoints.

mirror line
S3.2

A mirror line is a line or axis of symmetry.

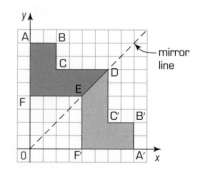

mode, modal
D1.2, D2.2, P1.1, D3.2, D3.3

The mode is an average that is the data value that occurs most often.
1, 1, 2, 2, 2, 3, 4, 5
The mode of these numbers is 2.

multiple
A4.1

A multiple of a whole number is the product of that number and any other. For example, these are multiples of 6: $6 \times 4 = 24$ and $6 \times 12 = 72$.

multiply, multiplication
N1.4

Multiplication is combining two numbers to form a product.
For example, $6 \times 3 = 15$.

negative
A4.3

A negative number is less than zero.

net
S2.5, S4.4, S4.5

A net is a 2-D diagram that can be folded to form a solid shape.

numerator
N1.1, N1.2, N1.4

The numerator is the top number in a fraction. It shows how many parts you are dealing with.

$\frac{3}{4}$ ← numerator

object
S3.2, S3.3

The object is the original shape before a transformation.

operation
A3.4, A4.7

An operation is a rule for numbers or objects.
The main operations are addition, subtraction, multiplication and division.

order
A5.1, D3.3

To order means to arrange according to size or importance.

order of rotational symmetry
S3.4

The order of rotational symmetry is how many times a shape repeats itself in one full turn.

origin
S2.1

The origin is the point where the x- and y-axes cross, that is, (0, 0).

outcome
D2.4, D4.1, D4.3, D4.6

An outcome is the result of an event or trial.

output
A3.4

Output is the answer produced by a machine or process.

p(outcome)
D4.4

p(outcome) is an abbreviation of 'the probability of an outcome'.

parallel
S1.1, S1.9, A4.8

Two lines that always stay the same distance apart are parallel.
Parallel lines never cross or meet.

Glossary

partition, part
N2.4, N2.5, N2.6, P1.6, D3.3

To partition means to split a number into smaller amounts, or parts.
For example, 57 can be split into 50 + 7, or 40 + 17.

pattern
A1.3

A pattern repeats itself.

percent, percentage (%)
N1.5, N1.6, D4.3

A percentage is a fraction expressed as the number of parts per hundred.

perimeter
S2.3, P1.5

The perimeter of a shape is the distance around it.
It is the total length of the edges.

The perimeter of this rectangle is:
1 + 2 + 1 + 2 = 6

perpendicular
S1.1, S1.6, S2.1

Two lines are perpendicular to each other if they meet at a right angle.

pie chart
D1.4, D1.5, D3.5

A pie chart shows data as sections of a circle.

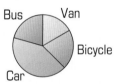

place value
N2.1

The place value is the value of a digit in a number.
For example, in 3.65 the digit 6 has a value of 6 tenths.

plan
S4.2

A plan is an accurate drawing of the top of a solid or of something, such as a room, drawn as if looking directly down on it.

polygon
S1.4

A polygon is a flat shape with 3 or more straight edges. For example, a triangle is a 3-sided polygon; a quadrilateral is a 4-sided polygon.

positive
A4.3

A positive number is greater than zero.

predict
B1.6

To predict means to say what might happen in the future.

primary data
D1.1, D3.1

Primary data is information you collect yourself.

prime factor
A4.2

A prime factor is a factor of a number that is a prime number. When you break a number down into its prime factors it cannot be broken down into smaller factors.
For example, $20 = 2 \times 2 \times 5$.

prime number
A4.2

A prime number is a number that divides evenly only by 1 and itself.

prism
S4.6

A prism is a 3-D shape that has the same cross-section all the way through.

This is a triangular prism.

probability
D2.3, D2.4, P1.1, P1.6,
D4.1, D4.2

Probability is a measure of how likely an event is.

probability scale
D4.2

A probability scale shows the probability of different events.

Impossible   Even chance   Certain

0 $\frac{1}{2}$ 1

problem
N2.8

A problem is something you need to find an answer to.

proportion, proportional
A2.1, A2.2, N1.1

Things are in proportion, or proportional, if they have the same scale factor.

protractor
S1.6, S1.7, S3.1

You can use a protractor to measure angles in degrees.

pyramid
S4.6

A pyramid has a square or triangular base and triangular sides.

quadrant
S2.1

A coordinate grid is divided into four quadrants by the *x*- and *y*-axes.

Glossary

quadrilateral:
delta (arrowhead), kite,
parallelogram, rectangle,
rhombus, square, trapezium
S1.4, S1.5, P1.5

A quadrilateral is a flat shape with 4 sides.

Rectangle

All angles are right angles.
Opposite sides are equal.

Parallelogram

2 pairs of parallel sides.

Kite

2 pairs of adjacent sides equal.

Rhombus

All sides the same length.
Opposite angles equal.

Square

All sides and angles equal.

Trapezium

One pair of parallel sides.

Delta (arrowhead)

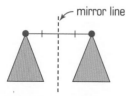

1 pair of equal angles.
2 sets of equal sides.
1 reflex angle.

questionnaire
D1.1

A questionnaire is a sheet of questions that you use to collect primary data.

random
D2.3

A selection is random if each object or number is equally likely to be chosen.

range
D1.3, D2.1, P1.1, D3.2, D3.3

The range of a set of data is the difference between the largest and smallest values. It tells you how spread out the data are.

ratio
A2.1, A2.2, N1.7, N1.8,
S3.5, S3.6

Ratio compares the size of one part with the size of another part.

rectangle
S2.3, B1.2

See quadrilateral.

reflect, reflection
S3.2, S3.3

A reflection is a transformation where the object and the image are the same distance from a mirror line.

mirror line

reflection symmetry
S3.4

A shape has reflection symmetry if it has a line of symmetry.

regular
S1.1

A regular shape has equal sides and equal angles.

represent
A3.1

You can represent a number or quantity by a letter. For example, you can use a to represent, or stand for, the number of apples in a basket.

right angle, right-angled
S1.2, S1.3

A right angle is 90°. A right-angled shape contains a right angle.

rotate, rotation
S3.2, S3.3, S4.1

A rotation is a transformation where every point in the object turns through the same angle relative to a fixed point.
One full rotation is 360°.

rotational symmetry
S3.4

A shape has rotational symmetry if when turned it fits onto itself more than once in a full turn.

round, rounding
N2.3, N2.5

You round a number by writing it to a given accuracy.
For example, 639 is 600 to the nearest 100 and 640 to the nearest 10.
To round to one decimal place means to round to the nearest tenth.
For example 12.47 is 12.5 to 1 decimal place (dp).

rule
A1.1, A1.3

A rule describes the link between objects or numbers.
For example, the rule linking 2 and 6 may be +4 or ×3.

ruler
S1.6

You use a ruler to measure lengths.

scale
P1.2, D4.2

A scale is a numbered line or dial.
The numbers usually increase in sequence.

scale drawing
S3.6

A scale drawing of something has every part reduced or enlarged by the same amount, the scale factor.

scale factor
S3.5, S3.6

The scale factor tells you how many times bigger something is.

secondary data
D1.1, D3.1

Secondary data is information that has already been collected.

sequence
A1.1

A sequence is a set of numbers or objects that follow a rule.
For example: 1, 4, 7, 10, 13, ... (+3)

side (of 2-D shape)
S1.4

A side is a flat part of a shape.

← side

simplest form
N1.1, N1.7, D4.4

A fraction (or ratio) is in its simplest form when the numerator and denominator (or parts of the ratio) cannot be cancelled any further. For example, $\frac{3}{6}$ in its simplest form is $\frac{1}{2}$.

simplify
N1.7, A3.1

When you simplify a fraction you cancel down to its simplest form.
For example, $\frac{3}{6} = \frac{1}{2}$
When you simplify an expression you collect like terms.
For example, $3x + x + y + y = 4x + 2y$.

solve
A3.3, A3.4, N2.8, A4.4

To solve a problem you need to find the answer. To solve an equation you need to find the value of the variable that makes the equation true.

source
D1.1

The source of your information is where you find it.

speed: km/h
A2.3, A4.9

Speed is a measure of how fast something is travelling.

$$\text{Speed} = \frac{\text{distance travelled}}{\text{time taken}}$$

square number, squared
A3.5

If you multiply a number by itself the result is a square number.
For example, 25 is a square number because $5^2 = 5 \times 5 = 25$.

square root
A3.6

A square root is a number that when multiplied by itself is equal to a given number. For example, $\sqrt{25} = 5$ because $5 \times 5 = 25$.

statistic, statistics
D3.2

A statistic is a value that describes a set of data.
The mean, median, mode and range are statistics.

stem-and-leaf diagram
D3.3, D3.4

A stem-and-leaf diagram is a way of displaying data.
For example, the numbers 4, 8, 13, 15, 16, 16, 18, 19, 27 and 29 could be displayed as:

0	4 8
1	3 5 6 6 8 9
2	7 9

Key: | 0 | 4 | means 4

straight-line graph
A4.5, A4.8

When coordinate pairs lie in a straight line they form a straight-line graph. Coordinate pairs from the same equation will make a straight-line graph.

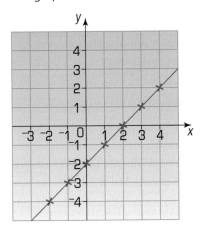

substitute
A5.2

When you substitute a number for a symbol you replace a letter with a value.

subtract, subtraction
N2.7, A4.3

Subtraction is the operation that finds the difference in size between two numbers.

surface, surface area
S2.5, S4.4

The surface area of a solid is the total area of its faces.

symbol
A3.1, A3.2

You can use symbols to represent numbers.

symmetry, symmetrical
S3.4

A shape is symmetrical if you can fold it exactly onto itself.

systematic
B1.3, B1.4, B1.6

To work systematically means to break a problem down into simple steps that you can solve individually. To list data systematically, you could arrange them in order of size.

table
D4.5

A table is an arrangement of information, numbers or letters, usually in rows and columns.

table of values
A4.5

You make a table of values when you plot a graph. It shows the values of x and y that you get using the equation of the line you want to draw.

tally
D2.1

You use a tally mark to represent an object when you collect data. Tally marks are usually made in groups of five to make it easier to count them. ‖‖‖

Glossary

term
A1.1

A term is a number or object in a sequence.
It is also part of an expression.

tessellate, tessellation
S4.1

Shapes tessellate if they fit together without any gaps.
The result is a tessellation.

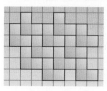

theoretical probability
D2.4

You can work out the theoretical probability of an event when all the outcomes are equally likely.

$$\text{Theoretical probability of an event} = \frac{\text{number of favourable outcomes}}{\text{total number of outcomes}}.$$

time
A2.3

Time is a measure of duration.
There are:
- 60 seconds in a minute
- 60 minutes in an hour
- 24 hours in a day
- 7 days in a week
- 28–31 days in a month
- 365 days in most years.

total
S2.3

The total is the result of an addition.

transformation
S3.2

A transformation moves a shape from one place to another.

translate, translation
S3.2, S3.3, S4.1

A translation is a transformation where an object moves a distance and direction. It is a sliding movement.

trend
D1.5, B1.5

A trend is an overall description of a graph or set of data.

trial
D2.4

Each result of an experiment is called a trial.

triangle: equilateral, isosceles, scalene, right-angled
S1.3, S1.5, S2.2, P1.5

A triangle is a flat shape with 3 sides.

Equilateral

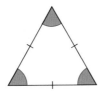

3 equal sides, 3 equal angles

Isosceles

2 equal sides, 2 equal angles

Scalene

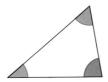

No equal sides, no equal angles

Right-angled

One angle is 90°, the other 2 angles can be equal or different

unlike terms
A3.1

Unlike terms use different letters and cannot be collected together. For example 2a and b are unlike terms. 2a + b cannot be simplified any further.

unlikely
D2.3

An unlikely event has a small chance of occurring.

value
A5.2, A5.3

The value is the amount an expression or variable is worth.

variable
A4.5, A4.6

A variable is a symbol that can take a range of values.

vertex, vertices
S1.9

A vertex of a shape is a point at which two or more edges meet.

vertex

vertical
A4.9

Vertical means straight up or down.

vertically opposite
S1.1

When 2 lines cross they form 4 angles. The angles that are not next to each other are vertically opposite.
Vertically opposite angles are equal.

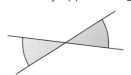

Glossary

volume: millimetre cubes, centimetre cubes, metre cubes
S2.4, S2.5, S4.3

The volume of an object is a measure of how much space it occupies.

width
S2.2

Width is a measure of an object that describes how wide it is. It is often used to describe one dimension of a shape.

 width

length

x-axis, y-axis
A4.5

On a coordinate grid, the x-axis is the horizontal axis and the y-axis is the vertical axis.

x-coordinate, y-coordinate
A4.5

The x-coordinate is the distance along the x-axis.
The y-coordinate is the distance along the y-axis.

For example:
Point A has
x-coordinate: 2
y-coordinate: 1

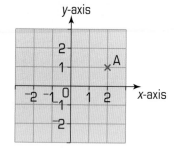

A1 Check in

1 a 20, 24
  b 7, 0
2 a 40
  b 42
  c 18
  d 16
3 a 3
  b 4
  c 4
  d 9

A1 Check out

1 a 25, 31   b 1.25, 1.5
  c 14, 11   d 10 000, 100 000
  e ⁻17, ⁻21   f ⁻4, 1
2 a 2, 6, 10, 14, 18, 22
    Start with 2 shapes and add 4 each time
    or
    the first term is 2 and the rule is +4.
  b 1, 2, 4, 8, 16, 32
    Start with 1 shape and multiply by 2
    each time
    or
    the first term is 1 and the rule is ×2.
  c 6, 11, 16, 21, 26, 31
    Start with 6 matchsticks and add on 5
    each time
    or
    the first term is 6 and the rule is +5
    or
    Number of sticks =
    (Pattern number × 5) + 1

A2 Check in

1 a 6
  b 24
2 a E
  b A = (2, 2), B = (0, 1), C = (2, 5)

A2 Check out

1 a Proportional, ratio of green to purple is
    1 : 2.
  b Proportional, ratio of yellow to red is
    3 : 1.
2 a (0, 0), (2, 1) and (4, 2)
  b (6, 3)

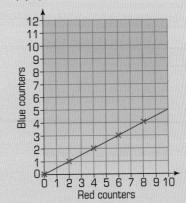

  c The coordinates lie in a straight line.
  d No
  e 4

N1 Check in

1 **a** 56
  b 18
  c 8
  d 8

2 **a** $\frac{1}{12}$
  b $\frac{2}{5}$
  c $\frac{3}{7}$

3 **a** 3, $3\frac{1}{2}$, 4, 5, 6
  b $\frac{3}{4}$, $2\frac{1}{4}$, $3\frac{1}{4}$, $3\frac{3}{4}$, $4\frac{1}{2}$

N1 Check out

1 **a** $\frac{1}{2}$
  b $\frac{1}{4}$
  c $\frac{1}{3}$
  d $\frac{2}{3}$
  e $\frac{3}{4}$
  f $\frac{2}{9}$

2 **a** 3
  b 4
  c £2
  d £15
  e £9
  f 30p

3 **a** $\frac{29}{100}$
  b $\frac{33}{100}$
  c $\frac{67}{100}$

4 **a** 7 kg
  b £4
  c £8

5 15 litres

A3 Check in

1 **a** 5
  b 8
  c 0
  d 6
  e 17
  f ⁻5
  g ⁻6
  h 5

2 **a** 28
  b 15
  c 48
  d 18
  e 7
  f 10
  g 3
  h 5

A3 Check out

1 **a**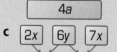
  b
  c
  d

2 **a** **i** $n+4$ **ii** $n+7$
  b **i** $m-2$ **ii** $m-8$

3 **a** 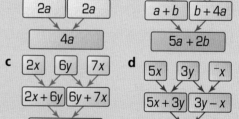   **b**
  c 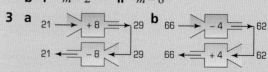   **d**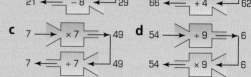

S1 Check in

1 a Angle *w* is obtuse, angle *x* is acute, angle *y* is a right angle, angle *z* is obtuse
  b Angle *x*, angle *y*, angle *w*, angle *z*

2 a 90°
  b 5 cm
  c 3 cm

S1 Check out

1 a 80°
  b 140°
  c 124°
  d 33°

2 a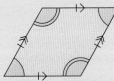

  b It has 2 equal sides, 2 pairs of equal angles and 1 set of parallel sides. It is an isosceles trapezium.

D1 Check in

1 a 2
  b 0
  c 0
  d Catherine

2 a Brown
  b 3

D1 Check out

1 a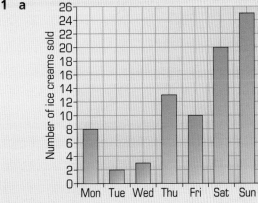

  b Sunday
  c Tuesday
  d Thursday
  e Tuesday and Wednesday
  f The shop sells more ice creams when the weather is warmer and at the weekends.

2 a 6
  b 6
  c 5.7

1 a A = (1, 4), B = (1, 1), C = (5, 1)

b y-axis

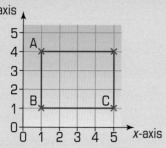

D = (5, 4)

2 a 40 cm^2

b 16 cm^2

1 a A = (3, 2), B = (3, ⁻3), C = (⁻4, ⁻3)

b

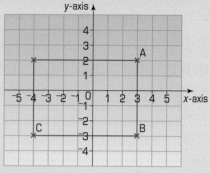

D = (⁻4, 2)

2 a 22 cm^2

b 29 cm^2

c 40 cm^2

d 34 cm^2

1 $\frac{3}{4}$, 3, $3\frac{3}{4}$, 4, $4\frac{1}{4}$, $4\frac{1}{2}$, 7, $7\frac{1}{4}$

2 a 0.7 + 0.3 = 1

b 0.4 + 0.6 = 1

c 5.1 + 4.9 = 10

d 3.2 + 6.8 = 10

3 a 370

b 8600

c 4

d 7.6

4 a 10

b 0

c 40

d 36

1 5, 5.5, 5.66, 5.9, 6, 6.3, 6.4

2 a 0.9 **b** 1.9 **c** 2.0 **d** 4.1

e 2.0 **f** 4.4 **g** 2.3 **h** 0.3

3 a 34 **b** 62.2 **c** 75 **d** 120

e 0.92 **f** 0.822 **g** 0.523 **h** 0.4

4 a 6.6 **b** 12.6 **c** 6.8 **d** 24.5

5 a 9 × 6 = 54 **b** 7 × 2 = 14

c 4 × 3 = 12 **d** 40 ÷ 8 = 5

e 32 ÷ 4 = 8 **f** 63 ÷ 7 = 9

A4 Check in

1 a $9 > 6$ **b** $8 - 2 < 7 + 1$
c $7 - 4 = 4 - 1$ **d** $^-1 < 0$

2 a

Input	2	5	7	9
Output	12	30	42	54

b

Input	2	5	7	9
Output	9	12	14	16

3 A parallelogram

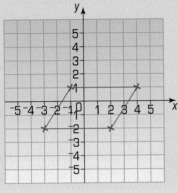

A4 Check out

1 a 4, 8, 12, 16, 20, 24, 28, 32, 36, 40
b 7, 14, 21, 28, 35, 42, 49, 56, 63, 70
c 28

2 a **b**

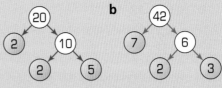

3 a $^-3 + 7 = 4$ **b** $^-1 + 6 = 5$

4 a

x	0	1	2	3	4
y	3	4	5	6	7

b

D2 Check in

1 a $\frac{2}{4} = \frac{1}{2}$
b $\frac{2}{6} = \frac{2}{3}$
c $\frac{2}{8} = \frac{1}{4}$
d $\frac{6}{9} = \frac{2}{3}$

2 a $\frac{1}{2}, \frac{2}{3}, \frac{1}{4}, \frac{2}{3}$
b b and d

D2 Check out

1 a

Number of people in household	Tally	Frequency
1	JHT	4
2	JHT I	6
3	JHT JHT	10
4	JHT JHT JHT	15
5	IIII	4
6	I	1

b

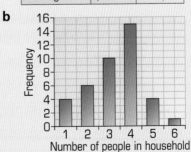

c 6

2 a 4 **b** $6 - 1 = 5$

3 a i It is impossible Jane will find a
household with 10 people.
ii It is certain she will find a household
with fewer than 7 people.
b $\frac{10}{40} = \frac{1}{4}$

S3 Check in

1 a ii
  b 4

2 a 2, 4, 6, 8, 10
  b 3, 6, 9, 12, 15

S3 Check out

1 a 150°
  b 48°

2 a Blue
  b Red
  c Yellow

3 3

P1 Check out

1 a £7.60
  b £74.40

2 a

		Spinner 1		
		1	2	3
Spinner 2	1	2	3	4
	2	3	4	5
	3	4	5	6

  b i $\frac{5}{9}$
    ii $\frac{6}{9} = \frac{2}{3}$

1 a $y = 4$
  b $y = 8$

2 a $16 + 2 = 18$ so $18 - 2 = 16$
  b $24 + 5 = 29$ so $29 - 24 = 5$
  c $12 + 9 = 21$ so $21 - 12 = 9$
  d $17 - 6 = 11$ so $11 + 6 = 17$

3 a $2 \times 3 = 6$ so $6 \div 2 = 3$
  b $10 \times 8 = 80$ so $80 \div 10 = 8$
  c $5 \times 6 = 30$ so $30 \div 5 = 6$
  d $28 \div 7 = 4$ so $4 \times 7 = 28$

1 a $x + 4$
  b $y - 3$
  c $2z$

2 a 1
  b 29
  c $^-3$
  d 13

3 a $W = T \times h$
  b £75

1 a 2
  b Wednesday and Friday
  c Tuesday
  d 23 cups

2 a 2, 4, 6, 8, 9, 11
  b 22, 23, 29, 33, 37, 42, 45

1 a

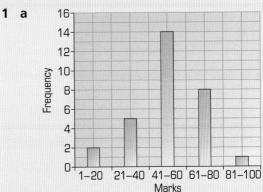

  b 30
  c 41–60

2 a Mode = 3, range = $11 - 2 = 9$
  b Mode = 42, range = $45 - 22 = 23$
  c Mode = 22, range = $93 - 18 = 75$

3 a Median = 8, mean = $40 \div 5 = 8$
  b Median = 10, mean = $50 \div 5 = 10$
  c Median = $\frac{4 + 8}{2} = 6$, mean = $36 \div 6 = 6$

1 **a** Equilateral triangle
   b Quadrilateral
   c Square
   d Octagon

2 **a** 15 cm^2
   b 8 cm^2

1 Net C

2 122 cm^2

3 84 cm^3

1 **a** Unlikely
   b Impossible
   c Likely
   d Certain

2 **a** $\frac{1}{13}$
   b $\frac{3}{13}$
   c $\frac{5}{13}$

1 **a** $\frac{1}{6}$ **b** $\frac{5}{10}$ **c** $\frac{4}{12}$ **d** 0

2 **a** $\frac{1}{6}$ **b** $\frac{1}{2}$ **c** $\frac{1}{3}$ **d** 0

3

1 **a** 12, 15
   b 19, 23

2 **a** 7
   b 9
   c 22

3 **a**

x	0	1	2	3	4
+3	+3	+3	+3	+3	+3
y	3	4	5	6	7

b

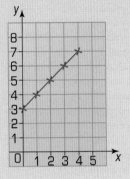

Students' own answers.

Index